Painless A/E Project Management:

How to Make More Money and More Happy Clients

By Frank A. Stasiowski, FAIA,
David Burstein, P.E., and
Michael D'Alessandro, P.E., PMP

Design Leadership Press
A Division of PSMJ Resources, Inc.

Painless A/E Project Management:
How to Make More Money and More Happy Clients

Design Leadership Press | A Division of
PSMJ | Resources, Inc.®
P.O. Box 95190
Nonantum, MA 02495
Phone: 617-965-0055
Fax: 617-965-5152
Email: customerservice@psmj.com
www.psmj.com
ISBN 1-55538-223-1

Manufactured in the United States of America.

ACKNOWLEDGMENT

PSMJ thanks Ernest Burden and Joy Arnold Burden for revising and editing this publication

ABOUT THE AUTHORS

Frank Stasiowski has authored dozens of manuals and guides serving the business needs of the A/E community, including eight best-selling books on management. In addition to being the founder and president of PSMJ Resources, publishers of the monthly newsletters *Professional Services Management Journal, PM Tactics, A/E Rainmaker*, and *PSMJ: Small Firm Advisor*, he is a frequent speaker at numerous prestigious A/E industry events such as the American Institute of Architects National Convention and the American Consulting Engineers Council. He is also the producer of METALCON International trade show.

With 23 years of in-depth experience in providing valuable information to the building and design industry, Frank speaks to and consults with design firms in the United States, Canada and Australia on such topics as Project Management, Negotiating, Proposal Writing, Presentation Strategies, Marketing Construction and Design Services, Client Driven Selling, Client Service, Strategic Planning and Ownership Transition.

Prior to forming PSMJ Resources, Inc. (formerly Practice Management Associates, Ltd.) Frank was the General Manager for King & King Architects, Syracuse, NY. His redesign of the firm's financial package led to a profile in Business Week and his first invitation to speak at the 1977 American Institute of Architects National Convention. While still with King & King, Frank helped to create a computer directory and seminar program for the architectural/design fields that would be the basis for A/E/C SYSTEMS show, which he and his partners launched in 1980.

Frank holds a BA in Fine Arts and a BA in Architecture from the Rhode Island School of Design and an MBA from Bryant College.

David Burstein has written and lectured extensively on the subject of project management. He co-authored (with Frank Stasiowski) *Project Management for the Design Professional* (published in English and Spanish editions) and *Total Quality Project Management*. David also served as principal editor for "Chapter 1: Project Management" for McGraw-Hill's *Standard Handbook of Environmental Engineering*. He has conducted over 100 seminars to over 3,000 engineers, architects and other design professionals.

David has nearly 30 years experience in the management of engineering companies including President of Parsons' 1600-person environmental subsidiary and President of Parsons 120-person planning subsidiary.

He is currently Director of Client Services for PSMJ Resources, Inc., the nation's largest provider of management information to the engineering/ architectural professions. As part of his responsibilities, he provides consulting and training services on the subjects of strategic planning, marketing, project management, human resources, quality, finance, and ownership transition.

David has BS and MS degrees in Civil Engineering from New Mexico State University and has completed the Crosby Executive Quality College program. He has been a registered professional engineer since 1974 and is a Diplomate of Environmental Engineering.

Michael D'Alessandro has been involved with the A/E Design and Construction Industry for more than 25 years. Prior to joining PSMJ Resources, Inc., he was with Parsons Infrastructure and Technology Group as a Principal Project Manager. His responsibilities included project management, proposal preparation, department management, and human resources management.

His extensive project management experience includes engineering, procurement, and construction (EPC) of industrial and municipal utility infrastructure facilities ranging in capital value from $1 million to $55 million. As a management consultant, he has provided project management consulting and training services to more than 400 AE firms.

Michael has a Bachelor of Science degree in Civil Engineering and a Masters Degree in Environmental Engineering. He is also certified by the Project Management Institute as a Project Management

Professional (PMP) and is a member of the American Society of Civil Engineers. Michael is also a registered professional engineer in a number of states and is a Diplomate of the American Academy of Environmental Engineers.

INTRODUCTION

W hen it comes to the ultimate success of a construction project, the buck stops with the Project Manager. Project delivery- on time and on budget- depends on the orchestration of a complex and demanding series of interrelated steps.

How can one person carry out the many and varied demands of the job? With a lot of help. *PAINLESS A/E PROJECT MANAGEMENT* is what every A/E/C PM needs to ensure successful project completion and ultimate client satisfaction.

PAINLESS A/E PROJECT MANAGMENT is a compilation of wisdom drawn from years of PSMJ Resources, Inc.'s publications, gathered into a single, very practical volume.

It is divided into twelve chapters:

    The PM's Role in Business Development

    RFPs, Proposals and Presentations

    Contract and Fee Negotiations

    Planning the Project

    Planning the Project Schedule

TABLE OF CONTENTS

CHAPTER 3

CHAPTER 4

CHAPTER 5

CHAPTER 6

CHAPTER 7

CHAPTER 8

CHAPTER 9

CHAPTER 10

CHAPTER 11

CHAPTER 12

CHAPTER 1

THE PROJECT MANAGER'S ROLE IN BUSINESS DEVELOPMENT

Do Marketers or Project Managers Bring In the Work?

There has traditionally been a push/pull that goes on between marketing and project management as to who is the lead in bringing in a project. Marketing directors say they have to chase project managers to get them to do write-ups for proposals. Project managers say they are spread too thin, and aren't trained to market. Is there an answer to this pervasive problem? The following comments are from veteran marketers talking about project managers, and seasoned PMs talking about marketers.

Marketer: "My involvement is mainly talking to clients, returning calls and e-mails, making sure clients get the service they want; those should be the duties of a project manager as well."

PM: "The most important thing is servicing the client, and becoming personal with them, since repeat clients are the best clients you can have."

Marketer: "I'm making sure our proposals are going out on time, and making new connections through existing relationships. There are also social events and personal connections, such as golf outings, dinners, attending conventions with our clients. In one week's time I can touch 10-20 of my clients all in one place, and it's all budgeted right into our revenue stream."

PM: "One of the most important roles of the PM is communication; going out and socializing, and developing that relationship with the project sponsors, and getting to understand how it's going to be handled, and preventing surprises. Every PM should have that responsibility if they're doing their job well."

Marketer: "Proposals are the best vehicles to show your wares, and you really need good marketing materials. Quality is everything. It sends a message to your client that you care about the project."

PM: "Part of our deliverables in proposals is scheduled meetings. We try to find reasons for clients to periodically look at the work we're doing, and see our faces. While we're sitting there, something usually comes up—and it often leads to new work."

Marketer: Marketing doesn't end until there is a comfort level with the client. You have to get the PM's involvement right up front. They need to be at the meetings and see the urgency of what's discussed. When they go back to the office, they're going to respond better. If you fall down at the beginning of the job, you've failed marketing."

PM: When we sign up a project we fill out a marketing form, the client, location, size, service expected. After a job is done, the same form asks; Can you take pictures, and was it successful? The photographer takes the pictures, we do a write-up that produces a project sheet that goes into our firm's marketing database.

Finally, are there as many opportunities for PM's to affect the marketing direction of the firm as there are for the marketers?

Marketer: "We hired a person to open doors and hold the client's interest in conversations, which I couldn't do; then, as soon as it got technical, our PM stepped in, and it worked like a charm."

PM: "A PM sits down with clients and their repre-sentatives all the time, and we have the opportunity to get a foot in someone's door every day. That has to be capitalized on to keep your company afloat and growing."

Use a Personal Action Plan to Get Your Project Team to Market

How do you persuade a project manager or someone in your technical staff to move out of the project delivery comfort zone and make time for marketing? One answer: translate practice goals into personal goals.

Marketing for the A/E is a very personal undertaking because the A/E practitioner is largely promoting personal competencies and commitment to deliver. Personal action plans are a powerful way to get people going. We all operate to some degree under a "what's in it for me?" philosophy. With those new to marketing, you can design the personal action plan around what motivates the practitioner. Plus, the personal action plan helps the marketer keep the individual's efforts consistent with the practice's goals.

Action Plan Basics

Every personal action plan should include these seven items outlined for the individual:

1. Keep a written record of all contacts and marketing "touches."

2. List personal goals.

3. Show the goals' link to the practice strategies.

4. Show the implementation tactics.

5. Keep an implementation time-line.

6. Show performance measurements or a description of what success should look like.

7. Have goals signed-off by the individual and a supervising or peer reviewer.

Peer Pressure

One key to keeping practitioners focused on their personal action plans is to make the plans public– internally, that is. This serves two purposes:

1. It puts healthy peer pressure on the practice member to set goals high enough to benefit the practice and to make a public commitment to achieve them.

2. It allows the practice group to review all personal action plans and offer constructive feedback if any personal plan is out of sync with the practice strategies.

An added benefit to using the personal action plan program is that these plan often become an organizing tool for the marketer.

The Benefits

The written plan helps you know where to support individual practitioner's efforts. Finally, these plans create a baseline against which to measure progress. When the individual succeeds, the practice should feel the boost.

Clients Are Digging Deeper for References

The importance of previous work for a client's educational organization cannot be overemphasized. If a client has dealt with your accounting staff, your principals, and your architects, they have a good idea if your firm can produce what it says it will produce. Educational clients also value that fact that you have worked for another university or government agency. It gives them another opportunity to talk to other people and find out more about your firm.

This was confirmed by a campus client in a private university setting:

"If you take on a smaller project, produce it the way it should be done and impress us, we will remember that, and if you come up with the proper team, it may not get you the job, but it will get you the invite.

"There may be firms that we don't know about, so we provide opportunities to meet the director of facilities or other people on the campus. We are more than willing to provide access to them, because in the end we're looking for the best value."

Looking At Remote Projects

Another public sector client commented:

"You have to be able to know the players, and know how people like certain presentations. Under the old system, if you did a really good job, you would always have work, because you made our project manager look good, so they would do whatever they could to convince the panel to use your firm. That's all out the window now.

"Also, in the past, if one of our PMs had experience with a firm on the list, they would have gone for the firms that they know. But the selection process is now monitored by procurement, not by our PM's favorite firm."

Another university client pointed out how they are able to check up on the performance of a firm on a remote project:

"When we read your proposals, we may not know some of the other firms you're listing, and we may have to do some investigation on a team member.

"If a project is listed in a proposal, or shown in a photograph, we will call and find out how the project worked.

"A good place for us to find this information is through the Society of College and University Planning (SCUP, www.scup.org). Not only do the facilities participate, but the financial institutions also participate. They use it as a follow up to check on your firm's credentials. You may have the credentials, but what kind of client satisfaction did you provide?"

Why Not Offer a Tour?

Another client commented:

"When we look at a remote project, we want to see how it relates to our specific building, size, program requirements, location, and how it fit into the campus. Sometimes we may embrace the fact that it is from out of the area, and look at it as a positive, in the overall rating.

"One firm laid out a plan for us to visit some of their comparable projects recently built out of the area as part of their proposal. We took them up on the offer and visited the sites. The projects were not identical but similar. This approach was very innovative, and put them a step above the others.

"We have to check with the SCUP associations' organizations to find out about a remote project. In this case, the SCUP checked their national association contacts to make sure that the building actually worked out for the university as well as the firm claimed. It did, and they were awarded the job."

How to Develop First-String Project Managers

You can't simply throw your project managers to the wolves and expect perfection. Strong PMs attain success and skill through practice, training, and the right amount of leadership.

Here are seven ways to put your PMs on a fast-track to firm principal.

1. **Encourage your project managers to be as direct and honest as possible in all interactions.** Remind them that if they're honest with clients, those clients will want to enter into long-term relationships with your firm. If your PM is direct about her ability to perform and not perform, she will inspire confidence in others.

2. **Increase your project manager's authority and responsibility.** This allow the true go-getters to shine. One Cincinnati engineering firm lets each senior PM be their own profit center. On each project, the company gets the first five percent of profit, but everything after that is split fifty-fifty between the PM and the firm. The PM's are in business for themselves. The result? Each individual "profit center" have turned out between 15 to 22 percent profit per year.

3. **Train your project managers to understand financial data.** Train them to read balance sheets, industry benchmarks, multipliers, direct labor ratios, etc. By giving them a bird's eye view of firm operations, you will undoubtedly see tighter project control and higher profits in return.

4. **Expect project managers to bring in new work.** If they're good, they will always strive to find new opportunities for the firm at all times. You need to continually emphasize this aspect of their job.

5. **Keep your project managers informed on industry trends.** Invite them along to association conferences and other seminars. Pass along industry publications and highlight pertinent topics. Even better—give an interested PM his own subscription. A good PM will have his finger on the pulse of industry trends and developments, such as new government regulations or project management software.

6. **Set high performance standards.** One civil engineering firm in Michigan keeps a list of 20

expectations for their PMs. For example, no PM can allow write-offs and error correction to be more than three percent of gross revenues per year.

7. **Don't micro-manage your project managers' projects.** They will never learn if you do the work for them. Also, they most likely have unique skills and talents that will come out with the right amount of freedom.

Don't Let References Checkmate You—Check Them First

References from past clients play a vital role in establishing immediate credibility with a prospective or new client. We often take them for granted, using old references, or worse, references that have not been surveyed for their current comments.

Consider these reference scenarios from different clients types:

First there's the *outdated reference*. As one client lamented. "We always make reference calls, and I can't tell you how many times firms submit a list of references in their proposal and the phone number is no longer working, or the person cited is no longer with the company."

Then there is the *silent but deadly reference*. A client was used as a reference for every proposal that went out. However, this person harbored deep-seated negative feelings about the firm, but never told anyone—only the people who called for a reference.

This brings to mind axioms about negatives that were compiled from a national study by the Technical Assistant Research Program, performed for the White House Office of consumer affairs. It states:

- Ninety-six percent of client complaints are never voiced.

- On average, each client will tell a negative story to nine other people.

- Thirteen percent of disgruntled clients will tell at least 20 other people.

The good news in this survey is that 70 percent of disgruntled clients will return if the design firm corrects the error, or apologizes for the problem.

Let's not forget the surprise reference. A potential client called a reference and received this response. "They did pretty good work, but we use another firm."

The client was astonished, and responded, "When your reference gives someone else a better reference, you don't rise to the top, the other firm does. That's a spontaneous reference, and it's very valuable."

Finally, there's the wild card reference, obtained by a client who doesn't believe your references. A developer client had this comment about how he handles design firm's references. "I believe in 'ground up' references. I call people I know and ask if they know anyone in the firm. If someone sends me a list of references, I throw it away because I wonder who isn't on that list. If I call the reference and don't know the person giving it, it's a waste of my time."

Outside Consultants

One would think that periodic needs assessments carried out by the PM would spot any problems—and it might. But past experience indicates that it will not. While readings on the progress of the work and the client's satisfaction is very important, the only true measure of a happy client and the potential for a good reference is found by outside consultants who are not part of the project's activities—good or bad.

Consider this verbatim reference acquired in this manner. "They're just tremendous folks to work with. They were always on call and always responded to those times I was available to meet, which didn't fit the typical 8 to 5 schedule. We have a major renovation job just underway, and I didn't even look at another architectural firm, because I've got a tremendous comfort zone in their ability to get that job done."

You can call this client anytime.

Make Project Manager Training a Priority

The following seven points provide a strong outline for a PM training program. Remember: training your people is a necessity that should be continued through good times and bad.

1. **Define what it means to be a strong project manager.** Identify responsibilities and authority by listing every key responsibility (scheduling, budgeting, negotiating, etc.) and list the most important traits a PM must exercise to accomplish the job (i.e., experience, communications). These traits translate into a good list of training topics.

2. **Separate task training from management training.** Too often PSMJ hears that a firm has a PM training program, only to find that the training is limited to such professional tasks as "energy-efficient design." Although professionally important, these subjects do not address managerial needs.

3. **Design a process.** With key subjects in hand, identify as many ways as possible to expose your PMs to these subjects.

   - Locate outside seminars that deal with these subjects.

   - Identify books and periodicals.

   - Implement in-house case study lunches dealing with past experiences around each subject.

   - Identify expert consultants and speakers for each subject.

4. **Budget for training.** Assess exactly how much billable time (annually) will be invested in each project manager's training. Larger firms usually allocate between 30 and 50 hours per annum, per project manager, for education and training. Also, include a fiscal budget for outside seminars, books, and publications.

5. **Vary the training.** Not everyone responds well to one type of training. Different types of programs include:

   - Seminars

   - College tuition reimbursement

   - Books and periodicals

   - Expert consultants

   - Brainstorming meetings

   - Visits to other noncompeting firms

6. **Measure the results.** Training isn't adequate unless results can be measured. Ask PMs to synopsize every seminar and report the key points to other PMs. Twice a year, have your managers hold a brainstorming session on the status of the training program.

7. **Additional suggestions**

   - Provide PMs with opportunities to improve, but don't force issues and expect overnight improvement.

- Keep in-house, self-run sessions as simple as possible. Deal with one subject per case, per session.

Use the appropriate level of training for each situation. For example, if you are covering a topic like financial management, keep it simple. Many PMs will never be financial managers, and complexity will turn them off even more.

Getting Your Technical Staff Marketing

Every good PM recognizes the need to bring work into the firm. However, many professional and technical staff team members are hesitant to get involved in marketing. When your team members express reservation, give them the help and encouragement they need.

When team members say:

"Marketing is not my job"
—let them know that no one person or department can bring in all the work. Marketing is everyone's job.

"I don't know how to market"
—give them pointers, and show them how you do marketing.

"Paying clients are more important than marketing opportunities"

—explain that you have to satisfy both demands. If you only worry about paying clients today, there will be no paying clients tomorrow.

"I'm a creative designer, I'm no marketer"

—point out that no activity requires more creative thought than convincing a prospective client that you are the right firm and the right design team for the job.

"There's no direct reward for marketing"

—make sure they understand that the reward is them getting to design the project.

"I'm scared I'll screw up"

—give them encouragement and coaching. Start them off with small, low risk marketing and business development assignments.

Once team members know that they are expected to be involved in marketing—and that you are willing to coach and help them—you'll begin to reap great results.

CHAPTER 2

RFPS, PROPOSALS AND PRESENTATIONS

How to Address Project Scope in Your Proposal

Most of the problems experienced during a project can be traced directly back to the scope of services. So a well-defined scope is key—not only to winning the project, but delivering it as well.

In every proposal, describe the specific tasks you'll perform. This is critical, since, in many cases, the scope becomes a portion of the final contract. Clearly outline, step by step, how you intend to do this project. Don't put "experience"-related language in this part of your proposal.

Use a work breakdown structure to organize the large, complex, overall project into logical work packages, and then into detailed task lists. You can assemble the packages on the basis of functionality, phase of the project, or any other basis that makes sense in this project.

The Work Plan

A good work plan doesn't have a lot of text. Rather, it spells out the details of your approach in lists, diagrams, budgets, schedules, and brief comments.

A work plan is composed of smaller "work packages." Overall, the work plan shows:

- What needs to be done, through the project definition and work breakdown structure.
- When it needs to be done, through the schedule.
- Who is responsible, through a project organization chart.
- How much it will cost, through the project budget.
- How quality will be assured, through a quality-control plan.

Examples of work packages include:

- For environmental work:
  - Monitoring well installation
  - Data validation
- For design work:
  - Conceptual design (phase-based package)
  - Preliminary sewer design (phase- and function-based package)

- Traffic analysis (function-based package)

Work packages can be based on your project approach, or they can respond directly to task lists or deliverables outlined in the RFP—whatever makes most sense to the client.

Once you divide the overall project into logical work packages, list each item required in that portion of the project. Describe the work packages and tasks briefly (so you don't lose the client in details) but with enough specifics so that both you and the client are clear on the services included. For example, if you're proposing on a feasibility study, you don't have to say that the report will contain a table of contents, but specify that the report will contain three alternatives.

Use bullet points instead of numbers. Numbers could be misconstrued as suggesting priorities.

Make sure you emphasize services that you provide the client free of charge. This doesn't mean you're giving away the store. It means that you can make marketing points by highlighting items you typically provide on any project.

Here are a few examples:

- Coordination of all subcontractors
- Chairing of all meetings
- Preparation and distribution of meeting minutes

When You Don't Have the Details

Sometimes you don't have enough information to write an aggressive, coordinated proposal. Maybe you're working through a prime consultant or through an environmental firm heading into a project with an uncertain outcome. Or perhaps the project isn't yet at the stage where you can define exactly what needs to be done. There are three ways to write a quality proposal and protect yourself at the same time.

Make clearly-defined assumptions about what needs to be done. Lay out a likely scenario and follow it through to its logical conclusion. Make it clear that you will change the proposal if the client chooses a different scope of work.

Propose a preliminary project whose objective is to define the larger project. This approach gives the client the opportunity to wait to define the ultimate project until preliminary work is complete. Taking this leadership role sets you apart from competitors. It's risky, but good clients will welcome the advice.

Mini-scope. Break typical tasks into "menu items" the client can choose from. List each service, with a price range.

The client can choose the necessary services. Thus, the client is responsible for scope. And down the road, if more services are required, it's obvious who made the decision to leave them out in the first place.

Features, Benefits, Risk Reducers

Firms seem to be feature rich, judging from their proposals and presentations: "We've done this; we've done that; we've designed more of these than anyone; we've been in business for 100 years." What the client really wants to know is how these particular features can benefit them, and how they reduce risks.

When creating a proposal or presentation, remember:

- Features are mainly self-evident
- Benefits need to be pointed out

Here are a couple examples of features, benefits, and risk reducers:

Example 1

- Feature: The ABC project was brought in ahead of schedule
- Benefit: The owner took possession of the property early and saved money.
- Risk Reducer: Our experience and procedures on your project will assure that your project will also be completed early.

Example 2

- Feature: The firm offers full in-house service capabilities and technical skills

- Benefit: There will be better coordination of the project

- Risk Reducer: There will be less chance for errors and you will get the latest solutions

Remember, every feature you offer begs the question, "What's in it for me?" The benefits provide the answer, and the risk reducer reassures the client of the benefits.

Benefits and risk reducers should be an integral part of every page of a proposal from the cover letter, executive summary, approach, resumes, to project descriptions. They should become the theme of your proposal.

Brainstorm Your Proposal Strategy

It's always preferable to work with a team to develop your overall proposal strategy, as one person working alone can easily miss an opportunity or key strategy. Brainstorming is an effective activity for getting the most out of group participation.

When brainstorming, use this step-by-step process:

- Gather the team for the specific purpose of brainstorming

- Define the goal of the session

- Through a brief discussion, make sure everyone understands the issue

- Have each person offer an idea. Either go around the table so that each person speaks in turn or encourage people to introduce ideas as they think of them

- Don't judge, evaluate or discuss ideas. The point is to collect as many ideas as possible

- Assign one person to record all the ideas on a flip chart.

- Group similar ideas together on the flip chart

- Prioritize the ideas

- Discuss pros and cons of each idea, then decide which merit follow-up

- Assign members to research ideas further, if necessary

- Set a date to reconvene

The Importance of Site Visits to Proposals

Those competing for a contract know full well that they need to go through the RFP more than once to create a proposal that is not generic, but germane to the project. The firms that don't make the cut are often those that send in a packaged response and don't show up to discuss the project with the client's representatives. Not showing up for client orientation or a project walkthrough is the kiss of death. Clients want to know that the project manager assigned to the project has been to the site. But more important, they want to know if the PM returned after the initial walkthrough. That activity is part of the dialogue that goes on before, during, and after the project.

It all has an impact on the selection process. It tells your client how hungry you are to get their work.

Research and Ask Questions

You have a strike against you when when you come ill-prepared on the issues you would have researched at the site and do not bring the team members that you are committing to the project. It's hard to come out a winner in this scenario. Granted, some small firms may not have the available staff to get out to the project site more than once. When visiting a site, ask as many questions as possible, and find out things about the project that will make you stand out when undergoing the interview process. Otherwise, it's all over for you. The principal of a small A/E firm in the Midwest attributes 25% of the success of an interview to what the team learned on site visit.

Other Factors to Consider

When clients are trying to determine which consultant will be best suited for their project, expertise in a particular assignment is the first criteria. This becomes extremely evident on a site visit. Other factors include your current workload. If you are buried in projects, clients wonder how they will be squeezed in. Also, MBE/WBE status on other jobs is critical in public sector work. Clients also factor in the geographic location of your office in relation to the project, as they will look for someone who can provide effective service in that area first. Travel is a significant and important cost, and the client would rather not pay for it, if it can be avoided.

Finally, the client may want to know details about the performance of the firms considered. The information for past performances usually comes from word of mouth on project managers, performance databases, or forms that get filled out on a project.

Bottom Line

The client's project management has an obligation at the closeout process to evaluate designers, consultants, and contractors. They need to complete projects on a timely basis and within their budgets. Many have a database where they track and enter the performance on the project, and that applies to all aspects of the project. Understanding the problems of a project begin and end at the site.

Proposal Strategies: Winning Versus Surviving

When you write the proposal with the objective of being selected based on your qualifications and experience, you run the risk of:

- Rearranging the requested format of the proposal to tell your story
- Concentrating on the features of your approach
- Ignoring the competition and what they might offer
- Ignoring any weaknesses you might have

On the other hand when you write the proposal to keep from being eliminated, you:

- Follow the checklist of criteria usually included in the RFP
- Add criteria assembled from your own research on the project
- Respond to each and every requirement in the solicitation
- Develop proposal themes that satisfy the critical factors for success
- Weave the themes throughout the entire document
- Offer a solution that solves the stated problem
- Tell them more than they told you in the RFP
- Emphasize the clear and direct benefits of your solution
- Provide direct answers to all questions, without any hype

Include the questions in bold or italic type along with your answers.

- Use bulleted lists instead of long paragraphs
- Don't refer readers to other sections to search for the answers
- Emphasize the benefits of your approach, and why they should hire you

Before you jump into writing the proposal, meet with your key players and go over every activity that needs to be done.

✒️ Proposal Planning Checklist

❑ Meet with the project team and discuss the proposal goals and objectives.

❑ Identify and discuss the key issues.

❑ Discuss the team's main strengths, and the competitor's main weaknesses.

❑ Review debriefing notes in a file copy of a similar proposal, either for the same client, or for a similar type project.

❑ Make notes and distribute to other proposal team members.

❑ Set assignments for any needed research beyond the RFP requirements.

❑ Call the client to discuss any inconsistencies in the RFP, if at all possible.

❑ Visit the site and take photographs.

❑ Identify the main proposal items and prioritize them.

📋 Proposal Planning Checklist (Cont.)

❑ Using the list as a guide, define all the team member's responsibilities.

❑ Outline these responsibilities on an organizational chart of the proposal team.

❑ Draw up a schedule for completing the proposal on time.

❑ Define the production resources you need: writers, graphic artists, printers.

❑ Communicate the scope of work to the team, and begin production.

❑ Revise and adjust the process as it progresses. Set up a way to communicate all changes to the proposal team.

❑ Review final production and prepare management to sign off before delivering it.

Make sure that a means is in place to get the proposal delivered to the right location, and on time.

Proposal Hot Buttons

Every client has hot buttons—stated or unstated. Here are seven of the most common issues to appear in RFPs, along with what the client actually wants to know:

1. **Time commitment and availability of project personnel.** Clients don't want the disruption that comes with regular team personnel changes. They also want to know that the team has a sense of urgency and personal commitment to the project.

2. **Your performance record on schedule (or budget).** The client's real question is, "What methods and techniques will you use to keep this project on schedule/budget?"

3. **Ability to estimate construction cost.** Your client cares as much about your cost-control methods for this project as about your past record.

4. **Design and conceptual sensitivity.** This issue surfaces most often in architectural projects. The client wants to know, "Are you able to listen and to understand what we want? Can you empathize with and hear what we are saying?

5. **Familiarity with public work.** Can you "schmooze" the funding and/or the approval process? Do you have the patience to deal with a building committee full of politicians and lawyers?

6. **Previous performance.** In every case, this means proven capability on projects identical to this one.

7. **Qualifications of key personnel.** This always means you—the project manager—and includes the level of interest you have in the job.

Coordinating the Proposal

Every proposal requires proper coordination early on. Use this list of questions for planning and managing the proposal effort. Reproduce and add to the list.

- Are we ready for the RFP when it arrives?

- Have we made arrangements to reproduce it as quickly as possible?

- Have we consecutively numbered the pages of the RFP (hand-written numbers) to allow us to easily reference any page?

- Have we run enough copies for the proposal team, project team, senior managers, and Red Team?

- Have all tasks been accounted for and assigned?

- Have we established a graphic standard for the proposal?

- Have page limitations been communicated to those involved with writing?

- If it's a large proposal, have we made provisions for bringing the team to one location?

- Do we have the facilities and equipment needed to produce the proposal?

- If not, do we have access to them at a reasonable timely cost?

- How are we going to communicate within the proposal team?

- What are our options for communicating with the client?

Proposal Self Evaluation Checklist

While it is imperative that you follow up every proposal with a debriefing with the client, you can also use the following items as a basis for developing your own evaluation, according to your specific client and project types.

❑ Does it respond exactly to the RFP and all the client's requirements?

❑ Does it reflect our complete understanding of the client's problem?

❑ Did the cover letter explore the client's "hot buttons?"

❑ Did the executive summary highlight the key points of our approach?

❑ Are there specific examples of successful related past projects?

❑ Does it demonstrate evidence of good management?

❑ Do all staff resumes clearly spell out successful related experience?

❑ Are the qualifications of the proposed project manager equal to the task?

❑ Is our technical expertise outlined clearly and concisely?

❏ Is the firm's capability to handle the project complexity demonstrated?

❏ Does it indicate that we can successfully meet the established milestones?

❏ Is the proposal logical, accurate, and complete in every detail?

❏ Is the proposal easy to read and devoid of technical jargon?

❏ Are the proposal graphics and illustrations professional looking?

❏ Is the prospect assured that the occupancy schedule will be met?

❏ Does the proposal demonstrate confidence that the project will be successful?

❏ What benefits would the client get by hiring the firm; are they out

How to Research Your Competition

Before you go into a presentation, you need to know as much as you can about who you're facing and how you can differentiate yourself from the others. Here are some ideas for researching your competitors:

- Search the Web.
- Talk to your closest client and ask questions.
- Contact their previous clients.
- Ask clients to tell you about past interviews.

- Ask clients to show you past proposals.

- Ask public agencies for their perception.

- Read their brochures.

- Obtain a Dun & Bradstreet Report

- Read the trade journals.

- Read their reports and work journals.

- Contact other consultants and contractors.

- Tap into your own well-informed grapevine.

- Canvas teaming partners for their perception and information.

- Call clients directly.

Scheduling Proposals and Presentations

Just like any project, proposal preparation requires a schedule—and the extent of the schedule depends on the length and detail of the proposal. Here are some guidelines for establishing a schedule:

1. Work backward from the proposal due date to the Red Team review (this review ensures you covered every item in the RFP). Allow a week for making any changes they suggest.

2. Work backward from the Red Team review to schedule work on the proposal. Allow the Red Team a week to review the proposal.

3. If the project is complex, create a chart that includes each task, the person assigned to each

task, and the deadline for each task to be
complete.

This schedule should be laid out and discussed with the
proposal team at the first pre-proposal meeting.

Presentations

For presentations, set up a schedule for your team
showing deadlines and who is responsible for what. Work
backward from the presentation date.

Schedule:

- A site visit; take photos if you have not already
  done so.
- Brainstorming sessions.
- The first draft.
- The review and approval of materials.
- Rehearsals.

Remember, when you schedule your actual presentation
time, request the last time slot. People remember best
what they heard last.

Presentation Rehearsal Techniques

Want to ensure every individual on your presentation
team will give the right answer during a Q & A session?
Try taking the following approach:

Require each presenter to meet with an individual not on the presentation team. Each "outsider" will ask the same questions of each presenter, and log their answers. This way, you can check to make sure each member is giving a consistent message. Come presentation time, you know your team will be unified in its message to the client panel.

By addressing your client's hot buttons through a well-tailored, well-rehearsed delivery, there isn't much else that stands in the way of getting the job.

Don't Discuss Your Competition during Presentations

Your presentation team has just delivered a smooth, succinct, top-notch performance in front of the client panel. During the question and answer session, you have responded to each question with clarity and confidence, knocking each question out of the park.

But just before the session ends, a panelist throws you a serious curveball, asking "What do you think of your biggest competitor?" How do you respond?

Do you discuss your competitor's shortcomings and past mistakes? While this approach may make your competition look bad, it has equal potential to make you look unprofessional.

On the flipside, do you tell the client how your competitor has a strong track record with great talent and experience? If you take this approach, you might as well hand the job over to your competition.

So what do you do?

Don't get snared in this trap. All you have to say is 'We don't think it is professional to comment on our competition.' That way, you don't advertise for the competition, and don't make yourself look bad by attacking their image."

Presentation Tips from a Professional

Here are some fundamental tips for making sure the selection panel remembers you:

1. **First and foremost, have a clear idea of your client's situation,** and let them know that you understand where they are, what they want, and what success looks like.

2. **Be polished.** At the end of every PowerPoint screen, summarize the page in one concise sentence.

   Selection panels typically sit through a full day bombarded with facts, data and information. Short and sweet keeps their attention.

3. **Use physical movement in your presentation.** Walk around, use hand gestures, and keep it lively. Too many presenters look rigid, with their hands folded or on their hips.

4. **Engage your audience.** Vary the tone of your voice, rehearse and tell a joke periodically, and try to appear as relaxed as you can.

Most panels don't expect architects or engineers to be easy to follow, so when you make these extra communication efforts, you will surprise your potential clients. All of these actions take practice. After brainstorming and organizing your presentation, you must take the time to monitor and critique each other's performance, and include someone directly involved in the presentation who can also monitor your performance.

Why the PM Should Lead the Presentation

The PM's role at presentations is more than just that of getting acquainted with clients—they should be running the show. Sure, your principal might start the presentation with an introduction, but after that, you should take control. When you speak in front of a panel, be sure to show confidence. Instead of describing "the team," refer to your staff as "my team." Exude leadership in every statement you make.

Leading Q&A

During Q&A, you are the ringmaster. You should be the one directing questions to the team member who can handle the question. Keep long talkers on track without reprimanding them. For instance, say "Kelly makes an excellent point, and I'd like to add to it..." You are then in control and can bridge to another point.

The best way to manage the Q & A session is to script it when practicing for the presentation. Anticipate every question that may arise, and don't assume the tough questions won't come up.

Take Charge during Presentations

Who should lead presentations? Principals and marketing VPs typically run presentations. Is this because they're the best presenters and the most convincing, or because they won't risk letting anyone else do it?

Clients Want to Hear From the Project Manager

Example 1–At a university building deliberation, one of the clients said:

> "Both AJA and HAR had their PM's running the show, and those are the people you're going to be dealing with day-to-day. The ability to see how they conduct themselves is very important.

> "It's nice to see executives, but the people who will be in the trenches carried the bulk of the presentation, with the others in a supporting role."

Example 2–In the deliberations for an engineering project at an airport, a review board chairperson commented:

> "We want a strong, local PM, and from the presentation we just saw, HJR had one. I was concerned that PB had a PM who might be in and

out periodically. He talked about breaking away from the project, which raised a red flag."

"I didn't hear much from Russ. He would be the lead PM, but he wasn't involved in the presentation. That leaves a question mark in my mind."

Show Enthusiasm

Example 3–A lead superintendent gave a spirited presentation for a construction project. The committee chairperson joked that it was too bad he didn't have more enthusiasm.

"I apologize, sir." was the reply.

"Don't ... it was very refreshing. I like your executives, but these are the people they're going to see. I commend you (superintendent) for carrying the presentation."

Want to win your next project? Get involved early in your proposals, and again in rehearsals for presentations.

From a client's perspective, managing the presentation successfully instills confidence that you will manage the project just as successfully.

Winning Presentations Put PMs at Center Stage

During presentations, clients keep a close eye on how teams function. "They knew their stuff at the presentation; I suspect that they'll do just as good a job on the project," is an often-heard comment from selection committees.

If you want your potential client to say this about your team, it should be you who takes control of the presentation. This doesn't mean you just get a chance to speak—you need to orchestrate the entire program.

The following example from a major presentation for the renovation of a historic bridge in an urban setting demonstrates this technique. The four firms involved were all equally qualified regarding past experience and expertise in bridge design and engineering, but the comparison ends there. How the PM's ran the show made all the difference.

Good, but Not Quite

The fourth-place team had a weak PM. He had plenty of experience, but was short on communication skills. His delivery was soft, speaking mostly to the scores of bulleted lists; and facing the screen as he read them verbatim. When he finished he abruptly sat down, and someone else continued without being introduced.

The third-place team was conducted by a competent but very young PM, who began by talking about the opening day of the bridge. His five minute segment of the presentation, where he named the engineers who designed the structure, and the mechanism for the bascule span, showed that the team had obviously picked the wrong PM for this job. He was later upstaged by a bridge consultants who said, "my greatest achievement is that this bridge and I are the same age."

The second-place team had assigned a transportation engineer to the project instead of a bridge engineer. He was a strong PM, and gave an upbeat delivery about the coordination of the team members. He discussed the schedule, team organization chart, and workload, and introduced the main project issues. However, he did not speak after that, and was overshadowed by others talking about the details of the project.

Taking Center Stage

The brief opening of the winning team was made by a Sr. VP who said, "You need a PM first and foremost who is a bridge engineer, who is local, and who has worked on the bridge before—that's Dave. He worked on the bicentennial inspection of the bridge, and we reserve him for the most important projects—like this one—and he's going to present the qualifications of the team members."

Dave did not look at the screen once during the entire presentation. He used the laptop as his teleprompter, and addressed the clients directly. He introduced every team member before they spoke, summarized after they spoke, and then directed the discussion to the next person. He was in full control of the presentation from beginning to end. He made sure that all client concerns were addressed. During the Q+A session, he directed all questions to the most appropriate team member to answer.

The team received unanimous first place votes from both the technical committee and selection committee.

Don't leave it up to the Sr. VP or marketing person to facilitate your next presentation. Client's are very clear about who they want to see conducting the presentation— and it's the PM who should be holding the baton.

CHAPTER 3

CONTRACT AND FEE NEGOTIATIONS

The Initial Negotiation Meeting

When negotiating your fees and scope of services, the first meeting with your client sets the stage. The ultimate success of the project may hinge on decisions made at this meeting. Use the meeting to establish guidelines, align expectations, and iron out potential stumbling blocks.

When information is shared during the first meeting with clients, you can develop a work plan, fee proposal, and terms that work for all parties.

Six of the most important items to discuss during your initial meeting are:

1. **Overall goals and concerns.** How will your client measure whether the project is successful? What are the client's fears, and how can you best assuage them? What pressures do the decision makers face (e.g., deadlines, funding constraints, community resistance)? Discuss any potential

obstacles you see. What do you need from your client to overcome these?

2. **Participants and responsibilities.** Review all key team members' project responsibilities. What disciplines are included on your team? Who are the client's representatives, and what are their expectations? Who among them has authority to approve decisions, and what information will they need from the consultants to make these decisions? Are there any consultants with whom your client will be contracting directly? If so, will your team communicate with them directly or through the client?

3. **Schedule.** Discuss milestones, funding deadlines, and other parameters. Advise the client of likely intervals between milestones. Identify potentials for schedule slippage, and discuss what can be done to avoid them. If the schedule is expedited, define what you will need from the client to meet the accelerated timetable.

4. **Scope.** What are your client's expectations? What tasks are typically included in your base fees? Agree on basic project parameters such as size, major components, and project or construction budget. Define the deliverables and the level of detail your client expects. Are there optional services not included in your basic scope for which your client wants you to propose fees?

5. **Fees**. Does your client have a range of fees in mind for your services? If so, how did the client arrive at this? What level of detail does your client need to evaluate your proposed fees? Use open-ended questions to gauge how much latitude you have.

6. **Agreement form**. Is your client amenable to using your standard form of agreement? Does your client have specific clauses that must be incorporated? Who will review the agreement, and can you meet with that person directly?

"You Have to Do Better Than That!"

One typical client negotiation tactic is to use the phrase "*You have got to do better than that.*" The client may use it routinely—whether or not he or she actually thinks you can do better.

The phrase, of course, immediately puts you on the defensive. If you find yourself in this position, try these four counter tactics:

1. **Ask for a price**. When a client says, "You can do better than that," respond by asking what price he or she has in mind.

2. **Caucus, and take a long time to come back**. If the client was bluffing, he or she will likely lose sleep over the time you are spending in caucus; you have now put the client on the defensive. When

you return, ask right away what price the client was thinking about.

3. **Change the scope of work**. If handled properly, a scope change can work for you. If the client suggests that you have got to do better than that, consider reducing aspects of your scope to meet his or her price demands.

4. **Use a value-engineering concept reflecting your fee as part of the project's lifetime cost**. Draw a pie chart showing your fee as less than one-tenth of 1 percent of the entire project cost over the building's 20-year life cycle. Suggest that by reducing your price further, the client will risk increasing the most significant cost of the project—its lifetime operating expense. Present benefits showing why you excel over your competition. Get the client to see the folly of reducing your fee by such a small amount when it could bring much higher long-term costs.

Training for Intense Negotiations

Any firm that aspires to be successful in the architectural, engineering and construction industry must include its project managers in the negotiation process. Negotiations conducted without PM involvement are at a disadvantage from day one.

The competitive nature of this ever-evolving industry mandates that you participate in client negotiations and learn how to do it effectively. You should walk into every negotiation knowing that you have done your homework. When planning for contract negotiations, ask the following questions.

Have you:

- Researched your client and determined his or her likely negotiation strategy?

- Determined your win/win or other negotiating strategy, with knowledge of your client's likely position?

- Chosen your negotiating team members, for their knowledge, roles, and negotiating abilities?

- Prepared your list of things you can trade to show concessions and gain concessions?

- Determined your walk-out position and made sure all on your team know it well?

- Determined whether you will be negotiating with client representatives who have authority to sign the contract, and set your strategy accordingly?

- Ensured that everyone on your team has a full understanding of your firm's objectives, your negotiating strategy, and the needs and likely strategies of your client?

- Tried to anticipate everything that could happen, and decided what you will do in each case?

- Included negotiating as part of your continuing education program in your firm, and studied other materials on negotiating?

- Had role playing and mock negotiation sessions, and videotaped them to review before starting a negotiation?

- Arrived with a pre-written contract and a pre-printed, small-type terms and conditions statement to attach?

- Committed to not leaving the negotiating table without signing any agreement reached?

- Prepared your key points and put them by your phone and in your briefcase, just in case you find yourself in a surprise negotiating position?

Before sitting down at the negotiating table, follow this checklist so you can walk into every meeting with confidence.

Seven Guidelines for Selecting Your Next Negotiating Team

Choosing the negotiating team is a critical step in your planning process for winning projects. There are no hard and fast rules for how to choose the right team, but there are some guidelines that will assist you in picking the right talent.

1. **Don't use too many people.** The optimum team will have three people: two who do most of the talking, and one who spends more time listening. The more people involved in the negotiations, the more difficult both the planning and the negotiating becomes. Remember, each member

has more than one role, so no one should go just to listen (a silent person prompts the other party to distrust your organization).

2. **Know the scope of services.** It's critical to include someone who fully understands the proposed scope. Usually, this is the project manager, but if there is someone else who understands the scope better, he should join the team.

3. **Have financial commitment.** Include someone with financial capabilities as well as the authority to commit the firm financially. This person can also ensure that everyone in the session has adequate information on financial questions and understands the economic impact of decisions.

4. **Have authority to commit to the contract.** If you have chosen a win/win strategy and you're negotiating with a principal from your client's organization, you must include someone who has the authority to sign the contract. The issue of authority is sensitive: if you send someone who can commit but the client does not, you may be forced to commit prematurely to items you would otherwise avoid.

5. **Know the client.** Someone on the team should have a full understanding of the client, as well as documentation of any promises made during the sales and marketing effort. Your marketing director or lead finder should be on the team or at least help prepare the team for negotiations.

6. **Deal with ambiguity.** During negotiations, many unresolved issues are in the air. It's important

that negotiators feel comfortable with ambiguity right up until the time when they're ready to sign the contract. Otherwise, they negotiate in a piecemeal manner.

7. **Keep Attorneys, accountants, and CEOs out of the negotiating team.** Attorneys and accountants slow the discussion and immediately put everyone on the defensive. It's better for you and your client to agree that either your attorneys will meet to clarify language or your accountants will look at the agreement later. It's also harder to wiggle out of a commitment if a CEO is on the team. Try to keep the CEO in reserve as the ultimate decision maker.

Communicate Better During Negotiations

One of the biggest problems discussed by many insurance carriers is the poor communication that takes place between clients and design professionals. Often this poor communication results in liability claims that could have been avoided.

To improve your communication skills, go over the following six points prior to entering negotiations:

1. Make a list of points of acceptable listening conduct. Is it all right to read a paper, write a letter, and so on?

2. What are your particular strengths or weaknesses as a listener? How do you listen?

3. Are there any mannerisms or gestures that cause you to turn off the speaker? Think of three mannerisms you do not like.

4. What words or phrases cause you to react negatively toward a person you are speaking with?

5. If you are listening carefully, think about how you act when you are listening. Likewise, think how you act when you are not listening effectively.

6. The next time you listen to a speaker, give particular attention to the opening statement and the closing. In a negotiation the first words uttered by the negotiator are very important. They set the stage for the entire negotiation.

How to Negotiate When the Client's Budget Is Less than Your Costs

No matter how well a scope is defined, there will be some situations in which the client simply cannot authorize enough money to cover all your costs, let alone allow for a reasonable profit.

In such cases, considerable ingenuity is required to avoid the dilemma of:

- taking the project at a loss, or

- declining to accept the project.

By using a combination approaches you can overcome this problem

Save Interest Costs by Improving Cash Flow

One way to accept a project at an apparent loss is to specify the proper invoicing procedures in the contract to improve cash flow. One such procedure is to include payment of a substantial retainer by the client upon project initiation. The entire retainer should be held until the final payment.

Another way to improve cash flow is to establish a weekly billing cycle based upon a pre-established billing schedule. For example, if a $130,000 project is scheduled to last 13 weeks, the contract can specify a billing amount of $10,000 each week. It is also useful to include a clause in the contract guaranteeing that interest be paid for late payment.

These approaches can cut the overhead rate substantially by reducing or eliminating the cost of interest to finance project expenditures. It may even be possible to create a positive cash flow, thus actually generating revenue from the earned interest.

Reduce Normal Overhead Costs

Another way to accept a project at an apparent loss is to reduce or eliminate costs that are normally built into your overhead rate. For example, if your firm allocates accounting costs to a general overhead account (as do most design firms), these costs can be reduced for a specific project by obtaining agreement from the client for a simple billing format with no backup documentation of expenses (such as copies of time sheets, phone logs or receipts). Under this kind of arrangement, the client can still be protected by being allowed to audit invoices on a random basis.

Work Overtime

Another approach is to take the project at a compressed schedule and work overtime. As long as the client agrees to pay for overtime hours at the same rate as regular hours, this can be an effective way to reduce the overhead rate because overtime hours generally do not carry the same burden as straight-time hours. For example, once the office rent is paid, it costs a little more to occupy the space 16 hours a day than it does for eight hours.

Lower Your Multiplier

If the client feels that your multiplier is too high, it may be possible to lower it by extracting some of the items as direct project costs. For example, professional liability insurance can be obtained on a job-by-job basis, with the premium costs being paid as a reimbursable expense by the client.

Another example would be to charge all labor and expenses associated with your firm's job cost control and billing system directly to the project. These kinds of measures, while not affecting the bottom-line project costs, can overcome the psychological effect on many clients of paying a high labor multiplier.

Receive a Percentage of Construction Cost Savings

Finally, if your client simply does not have enough money to cover your costs, you can offer to take the job at a loss, but include a provision that you will receive a percentage of the savings if the construction cost comes in under the estimate.

If the client responds with a request that you also pay a percentage of any construction cost over-run, point out that you have already taken a financial risk by accepting the contract at a loss.

Fifteen Tactics for Negotiating with Clients

Your participation in negotiations is critical. You are the person most familiar with the scope of work and the level of effort required to complete the project. Also, your presence demonstrates a symbolic "passing of the baton" from the principal or marketing people to you—the client's "go to" person.

Here are fifteen simple guidelines to make negotiations successful:

1. Attempt to promote a "win-win" situation.

2. Be prepared. Understand every detail and connection between scope, schedule, and fee.

3. Try to negotiate only with someone who has the authority to commit the client. When legal issues are raised, they are often best resolved between your firm's attorney and the client's attorney.

4. Prepare a confidential list of items that can be deleted from the scope of services without compromising the integrity of the project.

5. Never accept the first offer, even if it meets your goal. The other party is probably willing to make some concessions and you may come away with more than you expected.

6. Never give a concession without getting one in return. A concession granted too easily does not contribute to the other party's satisfaction nearly as much as one he or she struggles to obtain. In fact, it may cause the client to conclude that you were trying to take advantage of him or her.

7. When the other party makes a concession, don't feel shy or guilty about accepting it. Take it.

8. Don't lose track of how many concessions have been made. The overall amount can provide bargaining leverage. Keep tally.

9. Before negotiating, draw up a list of every issue. Establish an aspiration level, a minimum acceptable level, an initial asking price for each issue, and a "walk away" threshold.

10. Every concession should move negotiations closer to some goal. Spend concessions wisely.

11. Don't honor the opponent's unreasonable demand by making a counteroffer. Insist on a reduction in the initial unreasonable demand.

12. Don't make concessions with the goal of being equal. Some common sense negotiating goals:

Exchange little for much, now for later, little issues for bigger issues, and obscure items for clear ones.

13. Try to identify one minor issue on which you will make the last concession that will terminate the negotiation and achieve agreement. This allows your client to leave the negotiation in a positive frame of mind.

14. Remember that you will likely have to work with the people you negotiate with. Don't give them the idea that you are trying to extract every ounce of advantage. The goal is to reach an agreement that's fair and beneficial to both parties.

15. Never, ever, sacrifice the overall quality of the project.

Seven-Step Strategy to Negotiate Your Contract

When negotiating a contract, many clients want to immediately jump to the "bottom line"—the price! It is both foolish and imprudent on your part to respond to this request. Instead, as you negotiate a contract with your client, follow these seven steps in order, and make sure each step is complete before you move to the next one. Take as much time as you need. Whenever the client asks for the price, defer until everything else is clearly understood by you and your client. Whenever possible, don't reveal your costs, but quote a price that reflects the value of what you will accomplish.

Step 1. Define the project scope. Ask questions. Write down exactly what you will do as well as client expectations at each part of the scope. Break the scope into segments (or tasks) so that no segment represents more than 5 percent of the total. This helps everyone understand what your firm is providing.

Step 2. Set a project schedule. Ensure that all elements of the scope are reflected in the schedule and no more.

Step 3. Identify the project team. Name each person who will work on the project and what that person will do; estimate hours and the fees for each person, and the totals. Don't show these figures to the client; they're only for your estimate.

Step 4. Define work quality. Quality is somewhat subjective, but you must define some objective criteria. For example, offer three design alternatives making it clear that the client must pay for further designs, identify codes and standards, types of computer analyses, etc.

Step 5. Discuss project risk. Whether or not you discuss this with your client, you should analyze it within your own firms. Ensure that the party (you or the client) clearly understands who is responsible for each risk element. You might, for example, be taking the risk that this project will use all your people and you will have to turn down other work. Perhaps you have never worked on a project like this before, or are assigning less experienced people to keep fees low; or perhaps you need to provide for major changes in the scope once the project is under way. In any case, list each risk and determine who has responsibility.

Step 6. Make sure everyone understands the contract terms, specifically compensation, invoicing, change order process, payment timing, dispute resolution and indemnification.

Step 7. Quote the price. Quote a range for price if possible. This seven-step process should benefit both you and the client. If possible, you should establish this agenda with your client at the start of the negotiations so that you both understand the process. This will help both of you to cover all subjects (e.g., scope, schedule, etc.) that form the basis of the price before you are forced to commit to the price itself. Starting from the price and working your way back to the scope leads to unhappy clients and unprofitable jobs.

Get "Contingent Authorizations" for Scope-Increases

Do clients ever ask you to fit into your current budget additional services that they know to be outside your original scope?

On lump-sum contracts, you should obviously never do so. But what about time-and-expense contracts with a maximum? You may feel you can fit the additional scope within the current authorization, but don't do it! Instead, request a contingent approval.

A contingent approval is not really a contract. It should be just a letter saying something like:

Although we both agree that the services [described in your letter] are outside the original scope of services, we do not yet know if the current authorization is adequate to cover them. Therefore, no increase in authorization is requested at this time. However, should such an increase be needed, it is agreed that up to $_____ will be authorized for this scope increase.

The idea is to negotiate such an agreement anytime there is an agreed-upon scope increase. Then, at the end of the project, you can add up the requests in all these letters and make a case for requesting more money.

For example, say you reach the end of the project with a total of seven contingent approval letters signed by the client with a combined value of $34,000. But you may have realized some economies in other areas, resulting in a need for only a $25,000 increase to your not-to-exceed authorization.

When you ask for the lesser amount, not only will you probably get it all, but your proactive management will probably also make a big hit with the client!

(This information was provided by
David Burstein, P.E., PSMJ Resources, Inc.)

20 Questions before Setting Your Fee

Though many firms are walking away from low-price projects, you will always have clients for whom you must take on a project even though you cannot get the fee you want.

To help your staff tackle the go/no go decision on these, here are 20 questions I suggest you establish as a prerequisite to inking any contract.

1. What are our overall firm objectives?

2. What are our current and projected mixes?

3. How flexible is our pricing environment?

4. What do we want the price to convey?

5. What will it cost to produce this job (salary/overhead)?

6. How does our cost structure compare to competitors'?

7. What portion of cost is fixed? Variable?

8. How important is price to our client?

9. How much selective demand can we create?

10. Where is this service on the service life-cycle curve?

11. What non-price strategies can we use to redefine this service?

12. How many other firms can offer this same service?

13. How much will raising/lowering price affect profitability?

14. What is the client's time requirements?

15. Is providing this service essential to securing further work with the client?

16. Are we providing special expertise?

17. Where is the location and client?

18. How much will it cost to get this job?

19. Are there factors that may affect our payment?

20. Do we have the financial resources to sustain a loss?

Further, always negotiate price last. Follow this 7-step process and you can't lose on price:

1. **Scope first**. Make sure you and your client clearly understand project scope and set it in writing.

2. **Schedule drives price**. Always set target deadlines before fixing your price, and remember: shortening a schedule to aid a client is worth an increase in fees.

3. **Set the team**. Avoid uncertain and potentially costly results by agreeing on the team with your client before setting price.

4. **Set project quality**. Always quantify the "quality" you will deliver by limiting design time, the number of alternative studies, or the time frame.

5. **Know the risk**. If you take this job at a low fee, do you risk failing to deliver your best quality to your best client?

6. **Know the contract terms**. Never finalize a price until you do.

7. **Price**. Quote only ranges of fees until you get answers to all 6 items above.

Finally, on a price sensitive project, try to negotiate a "success" fee if you achieve something significant for the client/project, and always clarify how you are to be paid for changes during the course of the job.

Selling the Fee

Marketing helps to establish the expectation of what your fee should be. If your client perceives that you are begging for the job, the resulting fee will reflect it.

Be sure your marketers understand that the very first impression made on the client affects the fee you eventually get. A professional approach that focuses on how the firm can uniquely solve the client's problem is the basis for a commensurate fee.

A whiny, "we would be so lucky to get this job," attitude tells the client he/she can really ratchet down the fee.

This is another reason why you should compensate your marketers not on volume, but on quality. In other words, measure their performance on how profitable the work is, not how much work comes through the door.

Tips for Presenting Your Fee to the Client

Here are some handy guidelines for how to show your fee to the client:

- Don't put your fee in your cover letter or the executive summary. If reviewers don't like the fee, they won't read any further. Give yourself a chance to tell your story.

- Look for ways to reduce or remove the client's risk with regard to your fee. Think about guarantees (for example, if you don't return phone calls within six working hours, you deduct $100 from the invoice).

- Show enough detail to support your cost estimate.

- Quote a preferential rate if possible and explain why. For example, if the client gives you more than one project, you can reduce the rate because you have a lower marketing cost.

- Include management tasks in your fee for technical tasks.

- Use terms like "value," "stewardship," "earned value." Avoid "price," "cost," "fee."

- Consider trade-offs: a lower price if they agree to early payment terms; relax the schedule; agree to use your junior staff; reduce your risk or the project scope.

Client Perception of Price Is Reality

A client measures the appropriateness of a price by weighing the benefits offered by the package of services. Any difference in the nature of your package obviously affects the amount that client is willing to pay.

The client expects to pay more when he/she perceives that a desired service is available from only a few sources.

Different clients have different views on prices and services, and it is critical that you understand their views when going into a presentation. They may or may not be using price to eliminate competitors in the selection process, instead they may be using it to help set total project budgets, or to ensure that a limited budget can be met, or to justify their own actions to someone higher in the organization.

Your clients' view of price is affected by their perception of the supply available and of the value being purchased. Don't get trapped by the bidding process!

Take a Closer Look at Non-Standard Contracts

Many design professionals concede that they have unwittingly encouraged the use of onerous indemnifications by accepting them so readily. Fearing they might lose the job, the design firm disregards better judgment and signs an indemnity-laden contract.

But before signing on that dotted line, consider:

- Client-drafted indemnities typically ask you to assume liability for the client's negligence. Ask yourself: without the indemnity, whose risk would it be? Almost invariably it would be the client's risk.

- If you sign an indemnity agreement that is not limited to your negligence, you are accepting liability beyond that required by law. Your professional liability policy likely includes a clause with language such as: "This insurance does not apply to liability assumed by you under any contract unless you would have been liable in the absence of such contract."

- Client-drafted indemnities frequently contain onerous, overreaching language. For instance, a client may ask for indemnity for your "intentional acts." Unfortunately, a crafty attorney could interpret virtually any of your acts as "intentional."

- Client-drafted indemnities frequently ask you to defend the client. This provision could be interpreted as an obligation on your part to retain an attorney for your client and pay for this defense—even before liability for negligence has been established.

The PM as Financial Manager

Despite one's (primarily) technical background, a project manager takes on financial management responsibilities as part of his/her duties. Since any firm's profits are merely the accumulation of profits on projects, success depends upon these business abilities.

Consider the following financial role of a PM:

- **Budgeting:** Formulation of a business plan for a project is part of the PM's responsibilities. It should be a financial balance between professionally appropriate quality work and a client's ability and willingness to pay.

- **Profit making:** The PM's role is to produce the project as a cost that results in the planned profit.

- **Billing:** Clients should receive invoices for services promptly. Delays in billing are not the way to resolve technical issues.

- **Collections:** To operate, firms need cash, not completed projects. The best expression of confidence in the quality of one's work is to insist upon prompt payment for it.

- **Reviewing charges:** The project manager should see that all charges on a project are appropriate and that all appropriate charges are promptly made. This includes ensuring that sub-contractors submit their bills promptly. Don't be surprised by late charges. Good financial history on projects is critical for future budgeting.

- **Effectively using resources:** Clients are willing to pay professional fees that result in profits as long as they are not paying for inefficiency or waste. It is up to the PM to control the effective use of people, computers and other resources on the job.

- **Utilizing time:** Salaries are the biggest expense for any professional firm. Direct salary costs produce revenue; indirect salary costs drain profits. Project managers are responsible for seeing that their own time and their team's time meet utilization goals.

What Are the Financial Responsibilities of a Project Manager?

The project manager is a key player in ensuring that the financial performance goals of a firm are meet. The PM is responsible for managing projects but, to be truly effective, must also understand the firm's monthly financial reporting cycles and have the ability to plan, track, and evaluate each project's fiscal performance.

Here's a run-down of what your PMs ought to know:

- **Prepare the project budget and monitor its status.** The project manager must prepare the project budget and monitor its financial status. This includes ensuring that the information in the firm's management information system (MIS) is accurate and up to date. In large firms, a project administrator may prepare the various input forms, but the accuracy of this information remains the sole responsibility of the PM.

- **Monitor the work done.** The PM must monitor the work done or to be done. This should ensure that it is included in the authorized scope of services.

- **Seek additional fees for extra work.** When work is required outside the contract scope of services, the PM must seek additional fees from the client. When extra work is proposed, the project schedule must be reviewed to determine the effect the additional work will have on it. Most clients won't pay for extra work performed before it is authorized. A request for an increase in fees must identify any required work that's outside the contracted scope of services.

- **Get authorization for extra work.** This extra work must be identified promptly when it occurs, and the PM must notify the client in writing. Most clients won't pay for extra work performed before it is authorized. The project manager is responsible for ensuring that no unauthorized work is performed on his/her project.

- **Invoice clients promptly.** The PM is responsible for ensuring that clients are invoiced promptly and for following up on the payment of outstanding invoices.

Here are some additional responsibilities for the project manager:

- **Review time sheets.** PMs need to review weekly time sheets on a timely basis and ensure that corrections are made as required. Diligent review of weekly time sheets and project status reports will ensure that preliminary invoices do not need corrections.

- **Review preliminary invoices immediately.** The PM should be sure to review preliminary invoices immediately when they are issued.

  This review must:

  - Check the correctness of the client's name and address.
  - Crosscheck the preliminary invoice against the project reports for the time period being invoiced.
  - Check the correctness of labor rates and overhead percentages.
  - Check past due amounts and late payment fees.
  - Check that the total invoiced amount does not exceed the maximum fee.

- **Review all final invoices.** So as not to delay the monthly billing cycle, the project manager should review all final invoices in a timely manner. Diligent review of weekly time sheets and project status reports will ensure that preliminary invoices do not need corrections.

- **Prepare the letter to accompany client billing.** The PM needs to prepare the letter or required back-up data to accompany billing to the client.

- **Give the project administrator needed information for invoicing.** The PM must provide the project administrator with the format if any special invoices are required, or with directions and/or requirements for any specially prepared invoices on assigned projects.

- **Review subconsultant invoices.** The PM should review and approve subconsultant invoices when received.

- **Review invoices for other expenses.** When these are received, the PM must review and approve invoices for other expenses (non-labor) applicable to the project.

The Importance of Cash Collection Clauses

Cash flow to the firm is extremely important. Without a steady income, the firm must borrow working capital to pay its salaries and routine bills. This costs money and reduces profits. It is your job to ensure the client is paying in accordance with the contract.

Try to incorporate the following types of collection clauses or other similar language into agreements with clients. After getting them negotiated into the contract, make all efforts to enforce them—otherwise, why go to the trouble of having them in the contract in the first place?

- "Invoices for Services performed will be submitted to Owner by (your firm) monthly. Invoices are due and payable on receipt."

- "If Owner fails to make any payment due (your firm) 30 days after receipt of (your firm's) invoice therefore, the amounts due (your firm) will be increased at the rate of 2 percent per month (or the maximum rate of interest permitted by law, if less) from said 30th day; and, in addition, (your firm) may, after giving seven (7) days' written notice to Owner, suspend Services under this Agreement until (your firm) has been paid in full all amounts due. Payments will be credited first to interest and then to principal."

- "In the event of a disputed or contested billing, only that portion so contested may be withheld from payment, and the undisputed portion will be paid. No interest will accrue on any contested portion of the billing until mutually resolved. Owner will exercise reasonableness in contesting any billing or portion thereof."

- "Owner may make changes within the general Scope of Services in this Agreement. If such changes affect (your firm's) cost or time required for performance of the Services, an equitable adjustment will be made through an amendment to this Agreement."

Here is some alternative contract language that you might want to consider:

- "Client acknowledges that (your firm) will invoice once each month. If the client has any questions on the invoice, the client agrees to call the project manager within five working days of receipt of the invoice. Failure to call within this period acknowledges that the invoice is correctly rendered to the client and therefore payable within the prescribed time."

- "Our invoicing policy is that (client name) will be invoiced once a month for services performed during the previous billing period, normally four (4) weeks. Our invoices will be mailed no later than the last day of every month, and payment is due on receipt of the invoice. Should you require a different invoice submittal date, please so advise. Payment not received within 60 days of receipt of invoice will cause all work to stop on the project. Should legal action be required to collect payment, you will be liable for collection costs and reasonable attorney's fees."

Do You Understand Financial Management?

As A/E/C professionals, we all strive for success, and the indicators of that success depend on our focus. For us, the primary focus of any day's activity is the creation of design excellence. But this is subjective and, therefore, not an appropriate measure of how well we're actually doing.

There are other more appropriate factors. Among these are client satisfaction, peer recognition, zero-defect documents and effective project delivery. But the fact remains, no matter how satisfied your clients may be, or how many design awards your firm earns, or how many zero-defect documents you deliver, if your firm continuously loses money on its projects, it moves ever closer to demise.

Without profitability, a firm can't grow, nor can it reward employees for outstanding efforts or invest in state-of-the-art technology, and it can't then develop its staff and services.

Unfortunately, A/E/C professionals generally don't receive a formal education on how to run a business. If you're like me, you may have learned about financial management through on-the-job training or on your own time. Only a small percentage of our professional colleagues have continued their education and earned MBAs. As a result, the business side of our profession is generally left to specialists such as in-house business managers and bookkeepers, or outside financial consultants, who prepare the firm's financial statements and reports.

By delegating such business activities to others, a principal relies heavily on the accuracy of others work. This presents a dilemma if ever it becomes necessary to check the correctness of these statements and reports.

Today's highly competitive marketplace and the incredibly rapid pace of technological change demands that A/E/C principals be able to extract the critical data from their periodic financial statements. It's the ability to do so that allows strategic business decisions to be made in a pro-active, timely manner.

Bare minimum—to keep your firm on track with its goals and performance expectations, at the very least, you, as a principal, must be able to:

- Develop an annual budget

- Format and properly interpret the firm's financial statements as prepared by your CPA

- Develop the break-even and billing rates for every employee

- Develop the key performance indicators that identify your firm's financial stability

If you haven't mastered each of these tasks, it's time to get some training through your local community college or association.

It isn't necessary to have an accounting degree to understand such concepts, or to learn how to put them to use to enhance your firm's success (after all, practicing for prosperity and creating design excellence are not mutually exclusive goals). But sooner or later, the lack of a sound grounding in financial management will most certainly catch up with you.

Budgeting—Do You Aim for Low Risk or High Reward?

The estimation and monitoring of project finances is critical to the success of a project. Strictly speaking, budgets are models of a project's desired future performance. They don't exist in isolation, and many factors impact them, including time, resources, requirements, and quality. There are two budgeting techniques most typically used in the A/E/C industry, and project managers must recognize the differences and respond accordingly.

Top-down Budgeting. "Make it work..."

In top-down budgeting, estimates are determined at a senior management level, based on judgment and past experience. These estimates are passed down, sometimes after a contract has been signed, and then fine tuned by the project managers. This process is used to prevent the project manager from building an excessive scope or contingency into estimates.

Top-down budgeting creates rivalry between managers who are competing for fiscal resources and want to keep their own staff highly utilized. How- ever, this method does provide some stability to the budgeting process, and reduces the need for developing highly detailed estimates.

Top-down budgeting is often used on projects where the scope of work is not complex. However, if management's estimate is not very sound, the job can be a financial loser.

Bottom-up Budgeting. "Tell me what you need..."

Bottom-up budgeting is where elemental tasks are identified and hours are estimated for direct labor, then accumulated by task phase or activity type. Project managers sometimes work with their staff to have them contribute to developing production budgets and schedules.

These estimates are passed up so that management may review them, assign indirect and direct costs, a contingency, and a profit factor so that the final cost for undertaking the project can be determined.

With this method, it is imperative that all work elements get included. If tasks are overlooked or underestimated, then hours are either transferred from a contingency, pulled from other areas of the budget, assigned off project (i.e. the costs are eaten in overhead), or a PM can try to get additional funds from the client. To mitigate this risk, project managers often overestimate tasks to pad the estimate, just in case. This inflates the fee and can make a firm less competitive.

But...

The problem with each of these methods is that they are seldom based on quantified results from past efforts. They are usually based on subjective criteria, such as "this job is like that other job, how did we do that one?"

PMs often use criteria they feel more comfortable with, such as hours-per-sheet "rules of thumb." This is one reason why many firms perform poorly with lump sum contracts, the very jobs on which they should be able to achieve higher returns.

What's more, many project managers are unable to accurately gauge risk as they are not able to measure real costs. So they stick to what has worked in the past, assured that it won't get them fired for losing money. But the project does not make much money, either. If you take a low risk, expect a low return.

What Now?

In today's market, project managers must be more sophisticated in tracking real performance and preparing estimates. They must establish more detailed records of actual work effort on specific activities, not just in general activities like design development or drafting.

The adage "if you can't measure it, you can't manage it" rings true. Relying on simple time sheet data and rules of thumb is insufficient. Project managers must work closely with senior management and accounting staff to establish better project performance baselines.

Do this and you will have a highly valuable asset. Information. The kind of information that you can present a client and say with confidence, "Here is what it really takes to do this kind of work, and this is why it will cost this much."

And the kind of information that you can take to senior management and say, "Here is what it has really taken us to do this kind of work. We know where we can do better. Let's go after this next project as a lump-sum job, and let us show you what we can really do for this company!" Higher risk, higher rewards. You decide.

Value Pricing - Get Paid What You're Worth

Most clients are price shopping for services. Too many A/E/C managers still fall victim to psychological barriers to raising fees for fear of losing a project. If you are stuck in this dilemma, you are not alone. Here are nine ideas to help you "sell" higher fees to your clients.

1. **Focus on investment, not cost.** All too frequently, design professionals talk about "costs"—the cost of labor, of carpeting, of lighting, and the cost for our services. A change in the language you use can foster a change in viewpoint. Start referring to your fee as an "investment," and explain to clients that their "investment" will pay a high return in the value of their property or the improved productivity in their facility.

2. **Create an image that communicates "value."** If your image—which is a composite of how you dress, what you drive, how you respond to clients, and how you present past projects—screams "low price," clients won't think your services are worth more. Look expensive, and you will feel more confident about charging more. And you'll find clients who will pay more.

3. **Select the right clients.** If you accept work from economically deprived clients, you can expect lower fees. One Texas A/E/C actually asks clients for a financial background check before committing to work with them. And if you want wealthy clients, you must travel in their circles.

4. **Be straightforward about the business of your business.** Most A/E/Cs are incredibly sheepish about fee discussions. Break that phobia. Learn to be clear and concise about how you charge, the return clients can expect to receive for their money, and why you are a valuable investment.

5. **Never cut fees.** Trust is an incredibly important factor in the A/E/C industry. Imagine what a client thinks when you quote a fee and then quickly cut it. This sort of behavior leaves clients thinking you were trying to gouge them in the first place. If you must reduce clients' investment in you, tell them they will receive value that is commensurate with the investment.

6. **Win on contract terms.** Make sure that the terms of any agreement with your client include provisions that will reward you if changes occur after you start. Such terms could include payment for the client's switching representatives, for code changes, for special-event participation, and more.

7. **Get paid up front.** Any client who cannot pay you a small retainer up-front is probably going to be a problem throughout the project. Ask for at least $3,000 to $5,000 upon signing your agreement, even if it is simply a letter of agreement. Tell the client that you will credit the retainer to the last payment.

8. **Raise fees every year.** Now is the best time ever to raise your fees. To raise your fees, send a warm letter to all clients telling them that fees will go up in three months, but that for all projects contracted within 30 days, you will hold current rates for the entire project, as long as a 25 percent retainer is paid.

9. **Learn to walk away.** So now you've implemented all these ideas. If you are still being "nickel and

dimed," walk away. Convincing clients of your value starts with convincing yourself.

One Last Look at Your Budget

You should perform a project analysis at the end of every single project—and reviewing your final budget is an integral part of this process.

Final Budget Analysis

Your goal is to review the final costs on a task-by-task basis, comparing them to the estimates initially prepared during the proposal phase. You should know if overruns were performance-related or the result of poor estimating in the beginning.

Don't limit using your budget analysis to only projects that lost money. This analysis provides valuable information for creating better estimates for future proposals and projects—regardless of whether your project was or wasn't successful.

Try to include key members of your team in this analysis so you can obtain feedback on the original estimates versus the actual results.

Budget/Contract Analysis Checklist

In addition, you should answer and document these questions:

- Did the contract with the client contain all desired contract clauses?

- Did any problems develop because of certain contract requirements with the client?

- Did legal counsel review the contract before it was signed?

- Was the fee realistic, based on the types of service and risk assumed by the firm?

- Was the client advised of changes in scope and associated fee problems as quickly as possible?

- Was the available fee used to the best advantage of both the client and the design firm?

- Were extra fees requested for services that were beyond the scope of the agreement?

Raise Your Prices

Design professionals generally don't base their fees on the real value of design. Too many sell themselves short on every single project, with barely any profit left over. If you're busy now, raise your prices. You may lose a small percentage of work, but you'll make more money. The clients you lose are those you don't want anyway. One firm raises its prices by sending clients a price list on December 1, accompanied by a letter stating:

"Because you're one of our top clients, if you contract with us by January 1, we'll honor the prior year's prices. If not, please note that as of January 1, these are our new prices...."

This innovative marketing concept has two advantages:

1. It provides the firm with ample work for December (typically a slow month). This firm turned the least profitable month, —December— into one of its highest workload months.

2. It allows the firm annually to raise prices for most of their clients.

Raising your prices may yield less work, but it weeds out clients with payment problems who are usually the "nickel and dimers" of the world. These clients want the best price, don't have the money, and complain about the project anyway. By raising your prices, you'll be pricing your services out of their range. Life is too short to work for people who don't properly value your contribution.

How Do You Set Your Fees?

Do you set your fees based on your own pricing, or do you focus on the "market price" set by other firms?

If you calculate your fees based solely on your own costs and fees charged for similar work in the past, you may be proposing or charging fees that are well below market level.

And just how does one obtain fee information for other firms? It's not easy, but you can (and should) get your hands on outside pricing data:

The RFP and the contract award price are a matter of public record on all government contracts, local, state and federal. You may not be able to acquire detailed fee components, but you can compare the actual total price to what you would have proposed.

Many local governments must publicly record rate information when they enter into an open-end contract (you can find legal fees as well as engineering fees this way).

Ask your clients. When obtaining client feedback, you should ask how your fees compare with other firms your client works with.

Refer to industry surveys (such as PSMJ's *A/E Fees & Pricing Survey*) to determine how your rates, billing and contracting policies compare to those of other firms.

You should maintain "rules of thumb" (such as the percentage of construction cost) to use in comparing your cost-based fees to these guidelines. It takes work, but knowing how much your competition is charging is a basic and vital piece of your pricing knowledge base.

Basing your fees solely on the time taken and costs incurred on past projects is not an adequate basis for setting future fees. You may shortchange yourself, your partners and your employees.

Garner Higher Fees through Value Pricing

Value-added pricing strategies enable you to significantly increase the fees you charge for your services. While most

A/E/Cs are busy crunching complicated formulas to set "cost plus" fees, those firms that are making real money are talking with clients about solving their specific problems.

These highly profitable firms have learned to look at pricing in terms of "value added." They ask themselves: What value does my firm bring to the client's project?

If you can "add value" not provided by anyone else, you can bet that your client will pay the price you ask. The essence of value pricing lies in the strategies you use to promote, position, and package your services.

Firms perceived as providing the greatest value offer quality design, excellent service, and the highest level of flexibility in meeting client needs. The ability to sell value-added pricing also has a lot to do with your approach to business.

Are you the "break-even" sort of business leader who is content "getting by" and being comfortable? Or are you interested in the challenge of real growth and prosperity? If so, you have to lose your "break-even" mindset.

Value-added firms have the following qualities in common:

- They're innovative and not afraid of the risk inherent in a new idea—and they profit from implementing new ideas.

- They're quick to respond to changes in the marketplace and jump into new growth areas to find their own niche.

- They present their services in "bundles" of unique products that are priced and run as separate profit centers.

- They specialize—the easiest way to enhance "value-added." The most profitable firms specialize in both client type and project type, while the least profitable try to be all things to all clients.

Once you've decided to think in terms of the value you bring to your client, you can begin to negotiate price based on that added value. When the client asks for a price, defer until everything is clearly understood by you and your client. Whenever possible, don't reveal cost, but quote a price that reflects the value—to your client—of what you will accomplish.

Then follow this seven-step process, in order, and complete each step before moving onto the next.

1. Define the project scope. Ask questions. Write down exactly what you will do and what your client expects. Break the scope into segments, and make sure that no single segment represents more than 5 percent of the total.

2. Develop a schedule. Whatever format you use, go back to the scope and clarify anything that is not clear.

3. Identify the project team. Name each person who will work on the project, and specify what that person will do. Calculate the hours and fees for each person. These are for your use, don't show them to the client at this point.

4. Define work quality. Although this is somewhat subjective, try to define some objective criteria. You might, for example, offer three design alternatives, making it clear that the client must pay for further designs.

5. Discuss project risk and profit. Whether or not you discuss this with your client, it is something you should assess within your own firm. Either make a profit commensurate with the risk, or write terms into your contract that minimize risk.

6. Make sure everyone understands the contract terms.

7. Finally, quote the price. Shifting the way you think about pricing—and placing a dollar figure on the value you provide to your client—should enable you to increase your fees significantly and move away from a "break-even" business approach toward becoming a highly profitable firm.

Five Reasons to Turn Down a Project

The key to profitability is through setting high-profit goals, but you also need to be aware of those projects that could present unacceptable risk and leave you with no profit at all. Here are five reasons to turn down a project:

1. The project is too small. Every firm has a fee floor for profitability. A fee floor is generally determined by calculating the firm's liability exposure versus the amount of fee to be collected. Below this floor, your firm cannot produce profits, as it will automatically invest too many resources.

2. The project is too large. Any project that represents more than 25 percent of a firm's annual gross is too risky. Ask yourself whether, if that project is a failure, the whole firm risks failing.

3. The project is from the wrong client. Don't accept work from a client who is wrong for you, whether the reasons involve financial instability, litigiousness, or personality conflict.

4. The client won't pay. A strong reason not to accept a project is that the client is not likely to pay the bills. Assess the situation by understanding the nature of the client's industry and find out the client's reputation for on-time bill payment.

5. The project calls for expertise you do not have. Do not accept such work. You may be unable to meet your client's expectations and will probably subject yourself to unexpected costs, such as those for research and consultants.

Should You Take That Big Project?

At one time or another, most design firms have an
opportunity to land the "big job"—one much larger in
scope and required manpower than usual. It can be hard
to contain your excitement about such a project. But the
question is—should you take it? Before you commit,
consider the following questions:

1. **Is this work you want?** Does it match your firm's
   philosophy and operational style? Let the nature
   of the project attract you—rather than its size. If
   your firm favors quality, high-end design, you
   might want to avoid a sparing, traditional client.

2. **Will you be able to finance the accounts
   receivable?** Large projects inevitably mean delays
   in getting paid. Your firm will need the resources
   to carry receivables for longer periods than usual.

3. **What if they don't pay?** Consider the effect on
   your firm if the client were to default on the
   project and on payment. Would this threaten your
   firm's survival?

4. **What work will you sacrifice?** A very large project
   might mean you'll need to give up other work that
   could prove more profitable in the long run. Will
   the large-project client come back for more
   services—or use your talents one time only?
   Smaller projects with repeat clients may prove
   more valuable.

5. **What will be the effect on current clients?** Your
   business has likely succeeded by servicing a

stable of continuing clients. By taking on a large project, will you neglect the needs of your long-term clients? Big projects are exciting. Do not, however, jeopardize your current success by taking on a project that would compromise the quality of your service—or your reputation.

Using the Lowest Credible Scope Method

When pursuing most projects in the A/E industry, firms usually receive pressure from the client to bring down their price. In order to secure the job, some firms end up shaving their fee to the point where the price becomes unrealistic when compared to the scope. If you know this situation all too well, you may want to consider following the Lowest Credible Scope (LCS) approach.

You should use LCS to identify the lowest cost method to solving your clients' goals. Thus, you are pricing only the activities required to solve the problem. You are providing your client with the true baseline scope. You should give the project task list plenty of exposure so the client sees what will and will not be delivered. This also gives you an opportunity to talk about items beyond your scope, demonstrating your knowledge and experience.

Be very careful, however. If you offer the Lowest Credible Scope, you should not:

- Omit any task you believe to be essential to the success of the project.

- Lowball the price in hopes of earning more on changes.

- Deceive the client—ever, for any reason!

Seven Project Budgeting Pitfalls

When setting fees and creating project budgets, PMs often fall victim to the same mistakes. On your next project, pay attention to these common pitfalls when performing the following activities:

1. **Budgeting for corrections.** Most people budget for reviews, but are apt to forget that reviews almost always result in the need to make corrections. Identify reviews and corrections as separate activities in the task outline and budget for them individually.

2. **Budgeting for completion.** Even if all contract requirements are met, projects hardly ever end on the contractual date. There are, for example, questions from contractors, requests to attend city council meetings, requests for extra drawings. Include an appropriate amount in the project management task budget and plan to spend it after the other tasks are complete.

3. **Lowballing.** It's often tempting to take a project at a fee lower than the cost of doing the work, in the hope of obtaining a future fee increase. Just don't do it; it's too risky.

4. **Accounting for hidden costs.** It's easy to forget subtle items that are part of a typical project, like phone calls, travel time and cost, meeting with clients, maintaining project records, living expenses while on site, preparing reports, etc. Think through every aspect of every task and account for it in the budget.

5. **Budgeting for project management.** Many budgets fail to take into account that the project has to be managed. Budget 10 to 15 percent of the project costs for project management.

6. **Obtaining commitments.** Consultants should understand and abide by your budget. Negotiate the contract with a consultant as carefully as you negotiate with a client.

7. **Budgeting for contingencies.** Some firms go overboard on contingencies, trying to account for everything that could possibly go wrong and therefore pricing themselves right out of the contract. It's just as foolish to assume that you've thought of everything that could happen. Budget at least 10 percent of all costs for contingencies. Use historical data from your firm to establish a reasonable percent.

Would You Guarantee Zero Change Orders on Your Projects?

Sounds like a really dumb idea, doesn't it. After all, change orders are a fact of life, and clients must be made to understand that no project can realistically expect to be completed without change orders. Yet a Midwestern A/E firm challenged this conventional wisdom and is reaping huge benefits as a result.

This firm works mostly for school boards and public works agencies. Construction change orders are a nightmare for their clients. It's not because of the money, which is usually only a small percentage of the constructed value. It's because of the hassles they have to endure every time they take a change order to a board of lay people who think projects should be designed perfectly and that change orders are synonymous with design errors or omissions.

So this firm decided it would start offering its clients and potential clients a "zero change order guarantee" on new construction projects. (Renovations and expansions were deemed too risky for such a guarantee.) This guarantee covered all change orders regardless of cause, other than owner-directed changes. The terms of their guarantee are as follows:

- The client must agree to a very comprehensive subsurface investigation

- Construction bidders must be pre-qualified based on experience and prior performance on similar projects

- The design firm provides fulltime on-site resident observation of construction, paid as an additional service at the firm's normal office billing rates

- The client pays the design firm a "risk premium" equal to 2% of the estimated construction cost, payable upon signing the design contract

The design firm has been offering this guarantee for several years, with the following results:

- Clients are very impressed with the offer, whether they accept it or not

- Many clients do accept the guarantee as a way to cap their risks, both financial and political

- The design firm has paid out about 0.5% of construction costs to contractors in honoring this guarantee

As a result of this gutsy offer, the design firm has achieved the following benefits:

- Higher hit rate on proposals

- Additional fees for on-site resident observation of construction

- Expedited shop drawing reviews and reduced office costs for contract administration because much of it is done by their on-site representatives

- Extra profits equaling 1.5% of constructed value

- Greatly improved cash flow because the risk premium is paid up front and spent at the end

This design firm has achieved these results by not only performing design services but also providing "change order insurance," which clients value very highly!

Can Your Client Pay for the Work?

One of a project manager's worst nightmares is finding out at the end of the preliminary design phase that the client cannot afford to do all that was originally intended. When this happens, the client is not only disappointed but is also usually scrambling to devote as much money to construction funding as possible. Therefore, getting paid for redesign and/or value engineering efforts becomes more difficult than ever.

Here are some suggestions:

- Before beginning design, ensure that the client has a program of requirements and a total project budget including all costs, not just construction costs.

- Test the program and the budget for compatibility. Do not begin design until you are convinced there are adequate funds to cover all costs, such as construction, equipment, fees, moving, administrative, and finance costs.

- Verify the financial stability of the client via reference checks, as well as through contacts with other consultants who have had previous experience with the client.

The most important first step for a project manager is to verify the bonding and/or financing capacity of the client. In too many cases, a client may appear to have appropriate budgets authorized and allocated; however, the client may then learn that the financing markets will limit his or her financing capacity.

Profit—the Elusive Reward

Unlike labor costs and overhead rates, profit is usually negotiable with the client. The risk, complexity, magnitude, and duration of the project are all factors that should be considered during these negotiations—limiting of the firm's exposure to law suits or possible claims.

Complexity is often a factor in determining the percentage of profit. A complex project requiring unique and unusual skills or involving substantial coordination with many stakeholders deserves a higher profit margin than a simpler project.

Magnitude of the project—duration, depth of staff, and dollar amount—is often a factor. Larger projects usually have a lower profit multiplier than smaller ones.

Duration of a project can work both ways in determining an equitable profit. A short, intense fast-track project may require a firm to drop other activities, reassign staff, and intensely manage production. This compressed time frame warrants increased profit.

On the other hand, a project of long duration with periods of "hold" may require staff changes or assignment of staff to maintain their utilization. These projects are very hard to manage and should be reflected in the profit multiplier. Each project is different and other factors, some less tangible, influence the negotiated profit.

Check Your Fee Using "Percentage of Construction Costs"

What methods do you use to set design fees on a new type of project? Many firms set their total price by estimating the hours to accomplish each design and management task, multiplying the hours by the respective fee billing rates, and adding an amount for unknown risks and contingency. But there is another method that you should consider to check your final price—the Percentage of Construction Cost Method.

Sample Project

We've all been confronted by the following comment from a client: "We expect that your design fee will be about seven percent of the total cost of this project." To create an estimate of design fees as a percentage of construction cost involves a few basic steps:

Step 1: Breakdown the construction estimate by discipline. Assume the estimate for the total cost of a sample project is $10,000,000. Subdivide the total construction costs by the design discipline responsible for that part of the work. The objective is to ensure the estimated design fees are based on the construction cost of the work drawn and specified by each discipline. The information for determining cost breakdown by design discipline is readily available in the industry.

Step 2: Assign the appropriate discipline percentage to estimate the design fees. Determine an estimate of the design percentage fee for each discipline on the project.

These percentages can be determined from market survey data.

Step 3: Review and modify the estimate for risks and other factors. Review the results of Step 2 and modify the fee percentages for any specific project risks or other factors. Consider the following types of issues:

Individual discipline percentage fees generally decline as projects become larger. Smaller projects will have higher percentage fees than larger projects.

New construction projects differ from those that involve additions or reconstruction to existing facilities. Incorporating new design to any existing site or building is more difficult than working on a "green field" design. You should increase fee percentages appropriately.

The project or proposal team should perform a risk evaluation. Specific project risks accepted by the design firm should be quantified and their potential impact incorporated into the design fees.

Bottom Line

The Percentage of Construction Cost method provides both a check against the typical methods of estimating design fees and incorporates market survey data for the specific type of project being estimated into the equation. This method should improve your firm's ability to submit and negotiate better prices.

Never forget that setting the appropriate design fee for each new project requires a thorough knowledge of the scope of work, contract risks, and construction costs by major discipline. No matter how you format your fee proposals, these factors should form the basis for establishing the total fee for the project.

CHAPTER 4

PLANNING THE PROJECT

PM Procedures for New Projects

On all new projects, get off to a good start right from the beginning:

- **Budget and schedule before any work**. Wait until a firm budget and schedule for work is written down. Even for undefined hourly work, set a due date, and target a number of hours for every task.

- **Get tough on contract language**. Every new contract should contain a stop-work clause, a restart fee provision if work is stopped, automatic fee increases for work beyond a certain date, limits on liability, and procedures for payment to you on changes initiated by a client or outside agency not under your control.

- **Have a kickoff meeting on all projects**. Bring each client into your office, and meet with everyone who will work on the project—even administrative assistants. The objective is to have your team fully understand why the client is doing the project, what his/her expectations are, what quality is needed, and how critical the budget/ schedule is to the client.

- **Don't draw until the design is finished**. Another cause of project losses is repeatedly redoing working drawings due to design changes. To the extent possible in your practice, never start working drawings until design decisions are final.

- **Increase the frequency of project reviews**. Don't let projects go on for weeks or months without an appropriate client review. If you do so, you run the risk of having to change more drawings if things are not correct.

You need to refocus your attention on what has made your firm succeed—profitable and properly managed projects.

Project Kickoff Questionnaire

A well-organized kickoff meeting shows the team that you are in charge. Use the following checklist to make sure you are well-prepared:

❑ Has the final contract arrived?

❑ Does the signed contract differ from proposal phase info? Do we need more insight from marketing?

❑ Are job numbers assigned?

Project Kickoff Questionnaire (Cont.)

❏ Is the entire project or only a portion of the project authorized?

❏ Are task budgets (work hours) assigned and understood?

❏ Are key members of the team (internal and external) known?

❏ Is there a project management plan including schedule, budget, and client expectations?

❏ Are communication procedures in place for technical project work?

❏ Are client satisfaction checkpoints, interdisciplinary plan review checkpoints, and cost estimates scheduled (15, 30, 60, 90 percent)?

❏ Is all third party info identified and scheduled for delivery?

❏ Any unresolved technical issues, agency coordination, or confirmations that need resolution?

❏ Have all discipline managers and consultants confirmed their scope of work, schedule, and budget?

❏ Contract change procedures clear?

❏ Will the client require special invoicing preparation?

❏ Is there a quality control plan?

✍ Project Kickoff Questionnaire (Cont.)

❑ Will a constructability review be required (15, 30, 60 percent)?

❑ Is a site visit arranged for key staff?

❑ Has a schedule of drawings been prepared?

❑ Are there specified design checklists and computational procedures?

❑ Is the drawing index and filing system established?

❑ Have I initiated steps to form a relationship with the client? Is a client kickoff meeting scheduled?

Plan Right with a Project Task Outline

Here are five rules for building a detailed task outline.

1. **Start from scratch.** Always start from scratch when you are building a task list. Never depend on pre-printed, prearranged task lists, or modified lists from previous projects. Start at the beginning with the proposal and contract, and list each task that will be done throughout the project's execution.

2. **Keep it simple.** Excessively detailed task outlines invariably lead to a loss of control because project managers in most design firms simply don't have the time required to track numerous minor

activities or constantly update a complex task outline, schedule, and budget.

Give yourself a maximum of 15 to 20 tasks to cover the entire scope of a project, in the approximate order in which they will occur within the project. This simple outline is much easier to track and update.

3. **Maintain consistent use of the task outline.** When preparing the outline, use the same breakdown of project activities for:

   - The scope of services in the contract.
   - The project schedule.
   - The project budget.

This enables you to monitor project progress accurately, as each activity in the contract is measured in terms of progress made, time elapsed, and money spent.

4. **Define "what," not "how."** Every item on your task list should meet the expectations below:

   - Does it have a definable scope of work?
   - Does it have a defined duration, with at least one start date and one finish date? (some scheduling methods call for more than one start and finish date).
   - Does it have a defined level of effort? The level of effort is usually estimated in hours or dollars.
   - Does it tie-in directly to the contract deliverables?

Any item that does not contain all of these elements is not a defined task and does not belong in the task outline.

5. **After developing the outline for the first time, review it from several aspects to ensure it is properly prepared.** Ask the following questions:

   - Can I use the same outline to prepare the project schedule and budget?

   - Have I included all the delivery items specified in the contract?

   - Does each item meet the four criteria required for inclusion in the task outline? (see step 4).

   - Will the task outline require revision only if the contract is modified?

   - Is the outline general enough to accommodate routine changes in approach without being modified?

   - Is "project management" identified as a separate task?

Double-check Your Task Outline

After developing the task outline for your project for the first time, review it from several aspects to be sure it has been properly prepared. Review it against this checklist to make sure it will be a dependable tool as you manage the project:

- Can you use the same task outline to prepare the project schedule and budget?

- Have you included all the delivery items specified in the contract?

- Does each item meet the four criteria required for inclusion in the task outline (scope, duration, level of effort, and tied directly to a deliverable)?

- Will the task outline require revision only if the contract is modified?

- Is the task outline general enough to accommodate routine changes in approach without being modified?

- Can each task be specifically related to scope, schedule, and budget?

- Is project management identified as a separate task?

If the answer to any of these questions is "No," the task outline requires additional work before it can be considered complete.

Avoid "Scope Creep" With a Detailed Task Outline

Sometimes you don't realize that the client is asking for work outside of the scope of services until you are already over budget and off schedule. One of the best ways to ID "scope creep" is by referring to your task outline.

A task outline is the most critical element in good scheduling and budgeting, so don't skimp on its development.

A good outline should:

- Contain all possible tasks that can affect the schedule or budget of the project.

- Identify any tasks that will be assigned to subconsultants.

- Have a separate task for project management activities.

- Be "deliverable-based" rather than "task-or activity-based." The completion of the task should focus on specific deliverables so you can measure progress and completion easily

- Make the task outline the center of your system of project control. If you know your outline well, you will be able to notice when work moves beyond what was agreed upon.

How to Perfect Your Work Order System

One of the simplest and most effective tools for A/E project management is the project work order. Every project brought into the firm should have a work order developed prior to the assignment of a project or job number.

This work order should be written up by the person who committed the firm to the job. It should include:

- The client's name and address.

- The name and title of the client's in-house project manager or coordinator.

- The name, the title, and the address that should appear on the invoice.

- The date by which invoices should be sent out (coordinated with the client's payment cycle).

- The project start date.

- The quoted fee or project budget (expressed in dollars).

- The names of the principal-in-charge and the project manager.

- A week-by-week man-hour schedule of the projected work efforts by hours and by discipline.

This simple work order system becomes the basis for the project accounting system's billing process, manpower scheduling, and man-hour backlog calculation. Start with a fee budget on every job, and make it impossible to get a job number or a charge time without one.

CHAPTER 5

PLANNING THE PROJECT SCHEDULE

The 9 Most Common Mistakes in Project Scheduling

1. Failing to schedule time for the corrections that invariably result from project reviews.

2. Failing to clearly communicate to clients their responsibilities in maintaining the schedule.

3. Scheduling tasks to commence before all preliminary work has been done.

4. Assuming that all the work force you need will be available at the time you need it.

5. Forgetting about the "soft" tasks—non-technical duties like phone calls and meetings.

6. Assuming that all deadlines will be met and, as a result, not having a contingency plan for when they aren't met.

7. Forgetting about the fact that project activities continue beyond the due date of the contract.

8. Failing to obtain a commitment from team members that they can live with your schedule.

9. Assuming that all the activities in the schedule are under your control.

Consider Iterative Planning when Managing Your Schedule

Do you sometimes find yourself part way through a project when you suddenly acquire key information that would have helped you plan the project's tasks better? If so, you're not alone—after all, "things happen."

Projects typically unfold in unforeseen ways. One task might proceed quickly and smoothly while another might take longer and have lots of problems along the way.

By using repeat, or "iterative," planning, you can improve the overall project schedule.

Here's how you can plan to re-plan:

- Define the major (ten to twelve) schedule milestones.

- Choose those milestones that have specific meaning for the project team.

- Outline all the already-known tasks in the initial schedule for all of the project phases (preliminary design, code review, preliminary cost estimate, etc.).

- Specify criteria for each milestone. This way you will know whether or not the project has actually met those milestones.

- Plan the tasks needed to get to the next date. During the preliminary design phase, for example, you can refine the planned tasks and duration for the preliminary cost estimate phase.

- Build the re-planning activities into the original project schedule. Use this project's history to help update the project plan. In this way, the project team members realize the project is under control, and everyone can continually assess and manage the schedule risks.

At the start of the project, when the requirements are clarified and the actual programming is underway, plan the initial activities that will get you to your next milestone. As the project team understands more about the project, update the tasks of the initial phase as needed. Sometimes this happens as often as every day, but it's more likely to be weekly.

Plan in as much detail for each phase as possible, as early as possible; but remember, the plan and tasks are not frozen.

During each phase, plan the next phase's activities in detail. In addition to continually looking at your activities, measure how long the different tasks take and where the "faults" are. This process will allow you to start gathering data about your project while you're in the middle of it.

Throughout the project, use any "fault data" to continually re-assess risks and refine the schedule. By the time the project is in the detailed design phase, the schedule will be pretty solid, and you'll be aware of any potential project show-stoppers.

Iterative planning is not for everyone on every project. Use it under the following conditions:

- When you have an idea of what needs to be done but not a clear idea of how to do it.

- When you can take advantage of "project advances," or when tasks are completed in less time than originally planned.

Iterative planning and scheduling can help you on "bleeding-edge" projects, when you just don't have enough knowledge about this kind of project or historical data to plan the schedule with certainty.

This information was provided by Johanna Rothman, Rothman Consulting Group, Inc.

Turn Mega-Projects into Mini-Projects

Long projects can be daunting when setting a schedule. The project managers at the Wisconsin-based firm Plunkett Raysich Architects have found success chopping up big projects—some spanning three to four years—into smaller, mini-projects that are easier to manage.

Each mini-project has a distinct milestone to mark its completion. From the beginning, the project schedule is outlined with these milestones visible.

The mini-project deadlines are used to determine if the project is on target for the final completion date. If the project falls behind schedule on one of the early completion dates, the project team discusses how it can make up the time on the upcoming mini-project to ensure the final completion remains on schedule.

This approach makes goals visible and obtainable. If you are aiming for a vague goal that is three years away, it is difficult to remain excited about the project every day. But if the goal is four weeks out, clearly defined, and measurable, it becomes much easier to manage. Even when the team is facing upwards of 50 milestones on a project, there is a sense of emotional relief and accomplishment as the team reaches each milestone.

The Benefits of a Compressed Schedule

One of the best ways to ratchet up your profit is to compress your project schedules. The less time you have to work on a job, the less likely your are to put in more hours than you need to.

Whatever the job is, we tend to fill the time we have. It's human nature. So by compressing a schedule, you create a greater sense of urgency. You evaluate fewer alternatives and cut to the heart of the matter.

However, there is a caveat to this approach. Going into a project, you need to know your design criteria, top to bottom.

If you compress your schedule and allow for concurrent tasks, you will create something you don't want: rework. To mitigate that rework, it is critical that you decide on all features and design criteria early on in the design process. A designer might not want to decide on materials until he or she has lived with the project for awhile. But with a compressed schedule, another team member might, at the same time, be specifying finishes for walls. Later, you discover that the specified finishes are incompatible with the selected wall materials. The team could have avoided this if they had thought through the code issues and design components. Instead of addressing design issues as they come up, they should address them up front.

Shorten Schedules and Boost Your Profits

To increase profitability on every project, shorten the schedule by 10 percent. To do this, practice the following:

- Call a client today to reschedule a meeting 10 days earlier than originally planned.

- Re-examine drawings to eliminate unnecessary work.

- Contact a review agency to schedule two reviews simultaneously.

- Shorten specifications by 20 percent by eliminating unnecessary categories.

- Eliminate 10 percent of all upcoming project meetings.

For further ideas on how to shorten schedules, assemble your project team now and brainstorm more ways to cut the schedule specific to your project.

One Atlanta firm targets all projects to be complete within 85-90 percent of the originally planned time period, never informing the client of their scheme. Each member of the design team is then asked to submit one idea which can help shorten the schedule. By doing so, the entire team is involved in a thought process targeted to improve project profitability and eliminate wasted time.

If all projects are completed on this basis, the firm is naturally building in slip time that can be used to remedy a crisis if it occurs.

Top Five Scheduling Blunders

Your greatest challenge in creating a project schedule is to make it realistic. If you can account for all project components and gauge the time needed for each, you stand a greater chance of success. Below are five common mistakes that stand in your way:

1. **Forgetting to schedule time for review and revision.** Changes follow review like night follows day. But most PMs schedule time for review only. This spells trouble. For instance, if you were to schedule review by a building examiner one week before your bid date, you could risk uncovering a major code violation that could require big changes and a delay in bidding.

2. **Failure to plan non-technical tasks**—including phone calls from contractors, meetings with review agencies, or just general client "hand-holding."

3. **Failure to provide time for slippage.** All schedules slip, and you must plan for it. If, for example you allow no time for a designer to miss a deadline, you could create a chain of unmet future deadlines, causing frustration for your project team and client.

4. **Assuming that everyone will accept your schedule.** Without buy-in from the team, your schedule has no foundation. If you ask a team member to finish a task by Wednesday, that person must believe he or she can complete it in that time—and then must agree to it.

5. **Forgetting the critical role of the client**—especially for reviews, approvals, and sign-offs. Make sure the client understands his or her role in keeping the project on track. Always schedule time for client activities.

What Clients Want in a Schedule

There are seven things a client wants to see when you develop the project schedule:

1. **Authority.** Clients want to know that you have the authority to commit the firm and its resources to meeting the schedule.

2. **Involvement.** Clients need to be involved in the development of the schedule. Give your clients access to resources which can help to speed up the schedule.

3. **Commitment.** Clients want to know that you care about their projects. They want to know that bringing the project in on schedule is one of your highest priorities.

4. **Notification.** Clients like to be kept informed of developments—good or bad. Don't keep the client in the dark if something goes wrong with the schedule.

5. **Sense of urgency.** Your clients' money is tied up in the project. They want you to understand that schedule delays mean lost dollars.

6. **Consistency.** Clients want to work with the same team throughout the entire project. Switching team members and PMs slows down the project and reflects poorly on your priorities.

7. **A win-win situation.** Clients don't want to see you working 18-hour days to meet an unreasonable deadline. Clear communication from the begin-

ning can make for smooth sailing and repeat work.

Get Aggressive With Your Schedule

It is said that early identification of a problem is 80 percent of the solution. If so, this still leaves the other 20 percent to worry about. Consider these steps for overcoming schedule problems on a project:

Stop evaluating alternative solutions. When you reach a choice between several options, pick one that you know will work and go with it.

Get the less experienced people off the project. Senior staff are able to get more done if they do not have to spend time supervising trainees. You'll also be able to do more technical work yourself as a result of saving supervisory time.

Get permission from principals to postpone non-critical administrative duties until you have survived the crunch. Then spend the extra time on the most critical aspects of the project.

Subcontract a portion of the work to another firm. However, this is not the time to subcontract to someone you have not worked with before.

Identify the critical activities, and concentrate your efforts on them. Ask the client which items are most critical to them and if anything can be allowed to slip without harming the schedule.

Put in overtime. One study by a large engineering firm found that nine hours per day is the most efficient workday and that a firm receives only 10 percent productivity from the tenth hour and beyond. Keep productivity high by working Saturday and Sunday instead of working until midnight.

Why Wall Scheduling Makes Sense

Wall scheduling works best for projects with fewer than 100 tasks, or when 3 to 10 people meet for the scheduling session. Many firms report that clients and third party reps are among the strongest supporters of this scheduling method. So what makes it so great?

1. **Wall scheduling gets people talking.** During the meeting, conflicts are identified early, discussed, and resolved. At the same time, the team creates enthusiasm and momentum—more so than if you were to develop the schedule alone and present it.

2. **Team commitment comes easier.** When the structural engineer takes a card reading "prepare foundation drawings" and pins it to the wall at week 17, the commitment comes from that engineer and will likely be fulfilled. His or her promise is more reliable than if you were to demand agreement to a deadline.

3. **Wall scheduling helps communication.** In the meeting, you can give your team a comprehensive vision—let them know the project's larger strategic value for the client. The interaction

forces team members to fully understand the project's details, and how one person's task affects everyone else's.

4. **Wall scheduling helps balance project staffing.** Team members bring the knowledge of their workloads and commitments to the meeting, and are less likely to take on work that conflicts with other projects.

Seven Steps for Guiding the Construction Schedule

When developing scheduling guidance for new construction contracts, practice the following:

1. On most short term projects, require a bar (Gantt) for the construction schedule. On projects longer than three months, a critical path method (CPM) format schedule should be required.

2. Consider a cost-loaded construction schedule, with cost allocation for all component activities. Materials, labor, equipment, overhead, and profit for each activity should be indicated. Limit each activity to a certain value (e.g., $50,000) to provide adequate scheduling detail.

3. Make sure that dates for all required submittals to and all approvals from the design firm are defined in the contract and are included in the schedule.

4. Require that all anticipated dates of receipt and installation of all major items of equipment that are critical to the scheduled progress of the project be clearly defined.

5. Define the submittal and approval time of the construction schedule and all updated schedules in the contract. The construction schedule should be updated at least once a month. A narrative description explaining the assumptions and methods used to determine duration and sequences used in the construction schedule, (e.g., network analysis) should accompany the contractor's submittal.

6. Hold a site meeting to review the construction schedule and job progress at least once each month.

7. Make sure that all requests for time extension be justified by the construction schedule depicting the full impact on the critical pat.

Guiding the Contractors' CPM Schedule

For projects that require a CPM schedule, the following suggestions should be made to the contractor to help you in reviewing the schedule:

- The detailed construction schedule must meet the milestone dates in the prebid schedule. The calculated completion time must be within the time for completion given in the specification, and any intermediate milestone must be met by the detailed schedule.

- The schedule should include all submittals defined in the specification. Most construction activities are dependent upon submittal approval, and sequence of events usually begins with that submittal. If the time for your approval was not given in the specification, it should be agreed upon as shown in the construction schedule.

- The schedule should include major equipment fabrication and delivery. In many environmental projects, the specialized equipment represents the critical item in the completion of the work. The steps in the receipt and the installation of equipment should be clear in the detailed schedule.

- Make sure the schedule assigns responsibility for each activity, and be so arranged that schedules by organization can be printed separately. In many instances, the client, contractor, and subcontractors will benefit from having their activities isolated from a general schedule printout.

- Associate a dollar amount with each activity in the schedule. This allows the schedule to be used as a progress payment tool and a cash flow forecast for the client's financial planning.

- The schedule must define the critical path that limits the completion date for the project. There are often many delays on items that are not critical to the completion of the project. Unless the critical path of activities is defined, you cannot analyze a claim for delay.

CHAPTER 6

LEADING THE PROJECT TEAM

14 Critical Leadership Characteristics

Vision: Leaders create a vision for the firm and the future that inspires and motivates others.

Focus: Leaders spend their energies where they'll make the most difference to clients and the firm's success.

Values: Leaders "walk the talk," embodying the stated values of the organization.

Client Relations: Leaders understand what clients care about.

Empowerment: Leaders are coaches rather than managers, helping employees grow personally and professionally.

Inventiveness: Leaders offer a steady stream of new ideas, inspiring others to do the same.

Achievement: Leaders get things done. They maximize their performance and look for ways to maximize the firm's achievement.

Quality: Leaders strive to continuously improve the quality of their work and the work of others.

Energy: Leaders never tire.

Optimism: Leaders are positive about the future; they see obstacles as challenges to be overcome.

Teamwork: Leaders enjoy working with, and through, other people. They look for opportunities to praise the efforts of others.

Flexibility: Leaders perceive when their style or approach is not working, and they change direction.

Management: Leaders understand the systems and procedures that make the firm operate.

Courage: Leaders overcome their fear of the unknown.

Effective Leadership Style

If you're lost trying to decide which leadership style to use, your confusion may be over. Some leadership practices involve basics that good leaders use at all times.

Decades of research on leadership and management styles identified a popular concept known as the "situational" or "contingency" approach. Here, managers and/or leaders adjust their style for each situation they encounter, such as:

- The needs, wants, preferences, and maturity of the follower,
- The measure of the work being expected of the follower,
- The technology being used,
- The time required to make decisions, and
- The faith that the leader has in the judgment of the follower.

When it comes to "styles," many executives who use this "situational approach" to leadership can't articulate what they really do.

Take heart. Here are three keys to true leadership effectiveness:

1. Clearly define for your followers what your respective roles are, what their job priorities are, and what you expect them to do.

2. Clearly enforce whatever expectations you want to have met.

3. Make sure your followers can experience success for their efforts.

Beyond these fundamentals, successful leaders act the way their own personalities direct them. Most "followers" adjust to the personality of the leader as long as the three conditions above are satisfied. Often, people are more flexible than they are given credit for.

A "Take Charge" PM Checklist

As a project manager, you need to take charge of your projects. What clients look for today is leadership. What they want are project managers who can take charge and who have the authority to commit the resources of the firm.

How do you measure up? Ask yourself these questions:

❑ On each of my projects, do I have a clearly understood list of assumptions about what my client's expectations are?

❑ Have I communicated those assumptions to my people in a way that allows them to clearly understand their roles as they relate to the client?

❑ Have I clarified with the client and understood from him or her what is expected in terms of schedule performance and budget performance?

❑ Have I built into my schedules and budgets a factor of 80 percent or 90 percent for my targets?

❑ After a review, have I allowed for sufficient change time within my schedule and my budget?

❑ Do I understand that on every single project I perform, there will be some slippage due to changes within my firm, within the review agencies, and within my client's organization?

❏ Have I planned for, and do I expect changes in team members within every project that I'm working on?

❏ Do I have contractual terms in the project that will protect me if those team changes occur?

❏ Have I planned for, and do I expect massive changes relative to, finance on the project?

❏ Can my client be expected to refinance the project totally, if necessary?

❏ Have I designated a place where the team can get together and where I can leave information on a wall so any team member can check project progress, status, or changes?

❏ Do I have a "to do" list on every single project so I understand clearly what the issues are that need to get done on this project?

❏ Have I built in a list of priorities that are important to the team; for example, I will communicate on a weekly basis, or I will control my time through a proactive approach to time management?

❏ Have I established weekly, bi-weekly, or monthly project meetings with my clients to review project progress, ensure proactive leadership, and better manage my time?

❏ Do I have an established time to call my clients every week to inform them of progress on their projects and give them a chance to ask their questions?

After asking yourself these questions, evaluate your role as a project manager.

The Eight Traits of Top Project Teams

Research indicates that top performing design teams have these eight qualities in common:

1. **Urgency of purpose.** The best teams are driven by common goals so strong that these goals are almost bigger than life. The key question is how to create, enhance, or modify project goals to provide an overwhelming sense of urgency that each team member can own.

2. **Clear leadership.** Your leadership style often makes or breaks a project. You must be able to inspire collaboration within the team.

3. **A sense of place.** Sports teams have locker rooms. Armies have war rooms. Great project teams have a sense of place where collaboration can flourish. How can you create this in your firm when teams are constantly shuffled, sometimes even on a daily basis?

4. **Energy beyond 9 to 5 p.m.** Ask yourself, "What will it take to create an environment in which team members willingly 'forget the clock?'" Is age a factor? Or is it just the "team culture" that gets ordinary people to achieve extraordinary results?

5. **No rules.** Amazingly, our research indicates that most profitable firms have the least office

procedures. How can your firm overcome the gridlock of rules, manuals, and guidelines without losing control?

6. **No tolerance of non-performers.** Top teams will expel or ostracize non-performers quickly. This is a big problem for many design firms that keep some employees as long as they are "breathing."

7. **Highest ethical standards.** Honesty, directness, virtue, and respect are clearly evident in top teams. While everyone talks about these traits, the teams that succeed have principals and PMs who constantly emphasize ethical behavior.

8. **Fun.** An atmosphere of celebration abounds in top teams. People always seem to be fooling around, yet projects get delivered ahead of time with stellar quality. How can you inspire such activity without creating a circus?

How to Add Extra Spark to Your Team

- **Take a few moments at the end of the day to reflect on people whose performance you have noticed.** Write those individuals thank you notes, and leave the notes by their work stations as you leave.

- **Get away from your desk to see, meet, and speak with employees about work they are doing.** Take different routes in and out of the office.

- **Strive to create a work environment that is open, trusting, and fun.** Encourage new ideas and initiative.

- **Provide information on how the firm makes and loses money**, upcoming projects and market strategies into the overall plan.

- **Involve employees in decisions**—especially those decisions that affect them.

- **Give team members a chance to grow and learn new skills.** Show them how they can meet their goals and at the same time support the firm's goals. Create a partnership with each employee.

- **Greet individual employees by name and with eye contact.** Take a few minutes to see how they are doing. Be sincere.

- **Take time at the beginning or end of meetings to share positive news,** such as thank you letters from clients. Ask for praise between team members.

- **Make an effort to meet with team members you don't see or speak with very often.** Take a break together. Have coffee or an off-site lunch.

- **Act on good news!** Catch people doing something right and thank them for it—immediately.

- **Take time to listen.** Be responsive to people, not just problems.

- **Remember the 4:1 rule**—every time you criticize or correct someone, plan to praise or thank that same person at least four times.

Two Untrainable PM Traits

One crucial trait for a project manager to have is the ability to see the final goal and relentlessly impel the project towards it. In a word, a good PM must demonstrate a sense of urgency. He or she must see the bigger picture, so that setbacks, rather than hampering a project, become just curves in the road.

A project manager must own the project. A strong PM needs an entrepreneurial spirit, and an ethos of service. He or she must understand what drives the client and develop a passion for the client's long-term business vision. More than anything else, that passion will fuel a PM's sense of urgency.

A second key trait for a good project manager is a built-in sense of organization. When you walk into a PM's office, you want to feel that person has a plan and is working it, that he or she has things under control. You want to see well-managed to-do lists, meeting schedules, and file systems. You want to feel the PM not only can deal with a crisis, but knows how to stay out of one.

Urgency and organization: in this economic climate, they are what you need to deliver projects on time, and on the money. If you can find someone with these traits, you've likely found a good project manager.

But where will you find these traits? The problem is, you can't train them. They have to come naturally–so look for the signs. When recruiting, seek prospects who have competed—in sports, on debating teams, even in bands.

And find people who have served–in their communities, churches, or schools. Project managers serve their clients' needs and dreams. Make sure they fit the role.

Ask a prospect to show you how he or she plans a project. Does the person have experience in planning communications, risk management, personnel roles, and schedules? Will he or she be able to tell you if the project is on budget? How? In truth, a project is nothing but one series of crises after another. You want an organized, motivated, inspired PM to answer the call.

Every Effective PM Needs Authority

Clients want strong project leaders rather than mere project "administrators" who simply manage things and move them around. They want a project manager with the authority to push the project through his or her firm and commit the firm's resources.

Whenever a client must request something from a PM who lacks such authority, that PM must go back and ask permission, or wait and analyze before committing the firm's resources. The result: a schedule delay.

Irresolution can stop a project before it begins. For example, in the course of a sales presentation, the potential client might inform the team that his company would like to shorten the schedule by three weeks. If the PM lacks the authority to commit the firm's resources and declares that he or she must first go back and reassess how the schedule fits with the rest of the firm, the client will likely feel that the team lacks commitment.

However, if the next team's PM has full authority to commit the firm and can say to the client, "Without a doubt, I can promise you we'll take those three weeks out of your schedule"–which firm will land the job?

Although such commitment has its exceptions, truly effective project managers require a level of authority that gives them the right to commit their firm on a client need-by-need basis.

Effective PMs Need Multiple Abilities

While effective PMs must be empowered to commit the firm's resources in a reasonable and prudent way, they must also have the ability to:

- **Sell the project to the client.** The PM must have the skill to communicate the firm's ability clearly, succinctly – and with authority.

- **Motivate a team of design professionals and nonprofessionals.** This includes outside agencies, subcontractors, and consultants who must be roused to perform at their utmost in the client's interest.

- **Know when to take charge.** The project team is looking to the PM for guidance and direction. However, each team member must be allowed to exercise judgment and creativity within the constraints of the project and the team member's role.

- **Negotiate a fair and reasonable contract and favorable remuneration.** The PM must understand finance and serve as the last bastion of the firm's cash flow picture.

- **Accomplish rather than excuse.** Numerous excuses can be made for any project that does not meet budget, schedule, or quality needs. But the successful PM views difficulties as challenges and gains the respect of clients, supervisors, and peers by accomplishing the project's objectives despite any problems.

- **Serve the client.** The key phrase is "serve," not servile. The project manager must sometimes ell the client things he/she doesn't want to hear (for instance, that the cost to construct a favored design concept exceeds the budget). The ability to successfully manage client relationships is one of the project manager's most important skills.

- **Meet the schedule.** PMs must make it their job to see that everything possible is done to complete the project within the contractual time frame.

- **Make the planned profit on every job.** Every project manager must truly understand that in order to survive (not to mention prosper), design and construction firms must generate a profit.

Devote Time to Your Design Team

When PMs are asked, "Do you care about design?" The answer is a resounding "Yes!"

But, be careful about the message you may be sending your design team. When you concentrate solely on management issues, they may think you are not interested in good design. Similarly, when you do not work directly on the development of design ideas, the team may think you do not have time for them.

If you care about design—and all good PMs do—show your team. Set aside some time for the following activities:

- Involve designers in project planning. Set design objectives just as you would your budget, schedule, and quality standards.

- Include design as an agenda item at weekly project team meetings. Discuss design status along with all other project activities.

- Tell your team what your personal design objectives are for the project. Meet with the design team and let them know your observations about the design.

- Outline your weekly priorities and tasks for the team. Let them know that you are supporting design by the tasks you are accomplishing.

- Meet with your designers collectively and individually. Tell them what you think of their capabilities, and make sure they understand you have confidence in them. Do not let them think you do not care about design, simply because you are not looking over their shoulder daily.

PMs who care about design and let their teams know, ensure total project success.

Hiring a New Project Team Member

1. **Improve your interviewing.** The decision to hire a new team member is one of the most important you can make, so the interview is critical. Interviews are often too casual for picking the right candidate. Here's how to improve your interviewing technique:

2. **Review the candidate's resume in advance.** Check for inconsistencies in the record: Are there any gaps in the employment history? Has there been a lot of job hopping? Do the job descriptions seem inflated? Don't make the resume the interview focus; it should only help you decide whom to see.

3. **Prepare questions in advance.** Ask questions encouraging the candidate to talk about goals, qualifications and possible interest in your firm.

4. **Use the interview so the candidate can sell his/her qualifications.** Stress what they can do for you, not what you intend to do for them. Good candidates want to know how they can contribute to your success as well as their own.

5. **Maintain eye contact with the candidate.** Is the candidate listening as you speak? Watch for a positive attitude.

6. **Allow candidates time to ask questions.** They should have prepared questions if they've thought about the position and your firm.

7. **Describe your performance and compensation review procedures.** Are these agreeable to the employee? You must like the candidate's professional qualifications, but don't forget personality. Don't hire someone just because he/she is the only person available.

8. **Put it in writing.** When you have problem employees on your team, let them know it in writing. That way, you'll have documentation if a fired employee sues the firm. Here are two guidelines to follow with problem employees:

9. **Document regular performance evaluations.** Performance deficiencies should be spelled out and discussed with employees, and employees should sign their evaluations.

10. **Document specific instances when employees don't meet the firm's performance standards.** Then let them know:

   - What's expected to correct the problems ("We want you to do this").
   - What the firm will do to provide training/guidance/ assistance ("We'll help you to do this").
   - The consequences if they don't correct the problem ("If you don't do this, you'll be fired").

Here are suggestions that should help you to reduce the chances of an employee lawsuit:

- Ensure that job descriptions are clear, and outline performance standards and expectations.

- Provide frequent feedback to employees. Tell them if they are or are not meeting/exceeding expectations and performance standards.

- The employee manual should include a disclaimer that the manual is not an employee contract. Also, in most states, employee manuals should refer to the firm as an "at-will employer," meaning that it can terminate an employee at will, and an employee can quit at will.

- Remove any statements or agreements from the manual that say employees will only be fired for just cause.

- Ensure that employee benefit policies are clear and specific so they can't become an issue (e.g., an employee might interpret the accumulation of vacation time differently than you do because of a vague statement in your manual).

- Put it in writing; ensure that policies and standards are clear and concise. Write down employee problems when they occur. By doing this, you could "write" yourself out of an employee lawsuit.

- Improve your exit interview

- Find out how team members view your company by making use of exit interviews. The next time that someone turns in his/her notice to leave your firm, find out the real reasons for the departure.

- Use good interviewing techniques. Do very little talking and a lot of listening and note-taking.

- Ask exiting employees to be specific about what they liked and disliked about your firm. Find out where they're going, if they'll receive a salary increase, what their new responsibilities are, and what motivated them to make this change.

- Take good notes and circulate them to everyone, from the president down to the employee's immediate supervisor. Include specific quotes for greater credibility.

Nineteen Steps for Better Communication

Communication happens every minute of the day. It happens in phone calls, emails, face-to-face meetings, video conferencing, and in a variety of written and oral reports. How you communicate—whether through speaking or listening—can make all the difference in a successful project. Your firm depends on you to communicate effectively with your clients and your team.

The following list of tips compiled from PSMJ consultants can help. Keep this list handy, and refer to it before your next presentation, negotiating session, or team meeting.

1. Share all information relevant to an issue or decision.

2. Come to the table with no hidden agendas.

3. Seek timely resolution to issues.

4. Find out a potential client's preferred method of communication. Some clients respond better to written communication, while others prefer face-to-face discussions.

5. Accept responsibility for group decisions by showing your support.

6. Respect each person's contribution.

7. Be accessible. Make sure clients can reach you, and check your messages regularly.

8. Communicate effectively. Don't create surprises ("say what you mean, mean what you say").

9. Show commitment to tasks by attendance at meetings.

10. Review documents prior to each meeting.

11. Present agreements, disagreements and complex issues visually as well as verbally.

12. Speak concisely, give an overview, save details for questions or until your listener understands the big picture.

13. Use short sentences when writing or speaking.

15. Take notes. Writing down key issues of a conversation not only helps you out, it reassures the speaker that the message is truly heard.

16. Remember, we all speak a different language; don't assume your listener assigns the same meaning to your words as you do.

17. Practice the motto of "honesty is the best policy." Mistakes always occur, but dealing with them directly and honestly will build client trust and confidence.

18. Strengthen your speaking skills. Get rid of words such as "uh" or "you know." Consider taking a speaking class or seminar.

19. Ask probing, open-ended questions. Repeat what you think you have heard and seek clarification. Before responding, take the time to fully consider your reply. If you fail to communicate well, expectations may not be met, resulting in problems that take time and money to correct.

Regardless of the medium, to communicate effectively, express your thoughts and expectations in a straightforward, clear, and concise manner.

Does Your Team Know What's Going On?

You want your team to keep up with what's happening on the project. Here are three ways to ensure that team members stay well connected.

Every project needs a center, a "locker room" where the team can get together and find out the status of things. Without a separate space for the project effort, you'll have a fragmented team, with members operating in different areas of the office. This situation can inhibit team building. It can hurt your scheduling, budgeting, and project performance.

So pull your teams together. Give each project its own "team water cooler"—a physical space, or at least a central bulletin board. In this space, PMs can post a project "to do" list, as well as schedules and assignments. Team members can put up messages. Creating this team center will help build a sense of camaraderie and keep everyone dancing to the same beat.

Communicate!

Get people together at least once a week to talk about what's going on with their project. If a team has had no meeting for a month or more, you're asking for trouble. If it has had no meeting during its entire course, you're asking for disaster!

Team building takes communication. And communication takes the effort of the project manager to bring team members together at regular meetings to share what's on their minds.

Clarify your Purpose

The project "cause" comes out of the project manager's expectations for the job. Team members must know those expectations. Make sure your PMs share their objectives with team members at least once a week–the regular team meeting is the perfect time. Otherwise, don't be surprised by poor project performance.

When it comes to motivation, PMs may not have much more to do than create an environment supporting self-motivation. Your aim is to have your teams understand the project "cause" and rally 'round what the PM is trying to accomplish.

Give a Ten-Minute, On-the-Spot Training

Today, we are passing on more responsibility sooner to our younger, less-experienced project managers, project engineers, and project architects than did the previous generation.

It's great for those with initiative, but more and more we hear from the non-licensed personnel that what they crave most is on-the-spot training.

Look at it through the eyes of a younger employee. You don't have seniority, you're a team player, and you're constantly pulled on and off projects, doing small segments of work, often without seeing the final results of your efforts.

Employees suggest that what they need is a 10-minute customized training:

- Provide a brief overview of the project, its objectives, and how their work fits into the big picture.
- Then spell out the work expectation and what you want accomplished.
- Finally, and most important for interns and non-licensed staff, give the employees some ways to think about the problem and issues. They are the

ones who deliver the product and service to the end-user, your client.

Your project managers need a few hours of non-billable time each week to develop their employees. The payoff may be a well-trained and satisfied future work force.

This information was provided by Sandy Blaha, a consultant with PSMJ Resources.

Three Keys to Better Delegating

Saying it once is usually not enough. Hearing it once is usually not enough. As we move from simple military orders and simple tasks to complex assignments, we rely more on interpretation, independent judgment, and critical thinking for successful outcomes. This means that effective methods for delegating are imperative for the success of a project.

1. Communicate Clearly

When delegating, we may trust that a person has the skills to understand both a problem and a solution, and we often think it would be insulting to suggest that the person may not understand our point of view.

Unfortunately, this may be misplaced trust, not through a fault of the listener, but through a fundamental fault of our own—we expect the person to know what we mean in the absence of sufficient proactive communication of that meaning. Without clear communication of intent, the team member can only fill in the blanks based on his or her own personal experience.

2. Get Immediate Feedback

Feedback is essential to effective delegation. Immediate feedback communicates belief of understanding.

3. Monitor Progress

Even with proper communication and upfront feedback, a delegated job can go off course without proper monitoring. It is important to schedule periodic progress reports in order to ensure progress towards completion. If the delegatee in the example above is left unmonitored until the due date for the assignment, the supervisor may be surprised by the results.

Signs that You're Not Delegating Right Or Not Delegating Enough

Keep close tabs on how you delegate work as well as the success rate of the assignments you pass on. Make sure that you avoid the following delegating mistakes. Never:

- Let two or more individuals be responsible for the same task

- Overly structure the assignment so the individual has no latitude to make decisions

- Re-do the assignment yourself. Nothing undermines trust greater than this.

- Forget to thank a team member for quality work

Red Flags

You know you need to improve your delegation skills if:

- You're just too busy.

- You are under constant pressure, miss personal deadlines, or spend a great deal of time on activities that you would not personally pay your charge-out rate for.

- You're often surprised by team members doing things other than what you expected, and job quality is below the standards you expect.

- Productivity is low or dropping and team members seem less efficient and unmotivated.

Ten Steps for Successful Delegating

Delegating is the secret to getting your life back. While you might be able to perform the task faster than the delegatee, the team member will only become more efficient after practice. In the end, he will have learned a new skill, and you will have more time to spend on larger issues.

Here's 10 steps to better delegation:

1. Select the right person for the job.

2. Provide all the available information.

3. Ask what additional information is needed.

4. Clearly define the product you expect (scope, schedule, budget).

5. Agree on the proper approach, but don't confuse "different" with "wrong." The delegatee may have a better way to get the job done.

6. Agree on a completion date.

7. Agree on a level of effort.

8. Establish control mechanisms. (manage by walking around, by asking questions.)

9. Expect the product to be 30 percent different, and 10 percent wrong.

10. Give credit; take blame.

What a Major Industry Player Has Learned about Work Sharing

With today's demand for superior employees, you must be flexible in your staffing. The growing practice of work sharing lets you apportion your best resources—your people—and turn out excellent work cost-effectively. Communication and commitment will get you the results you want.

Situation

A 33-office, 1600-employee, worldwide engineering firm has relied on work sharing (borrowing staff or transferring entire project tasks between offices) to balance its workload.

After logging many work sharing hours, the firm conducted a study with its office managers to learn what worked and what didn't about this potentially effective approach. A subsequent internal report revealed some noteworthy problems—and solutions.

Problems

The firm identified five problems most frequently encountered during work sharing arrangements:

1. **Poor planning**–Inadequate cross-firm support creates personnel problems. An office might, one week, reject a qualified employee from a sister office and, the next week, advertise outside for qualifications previously rejected. Also, short-term out-of-office assignments make for difficult scheduling and commitment.

2. **Poor communication**–Informal communications make it hard to evaluate work performed by another office.

3. **Poor treatment of sister offices**–A reduced sense of urgency results in neglect of projects coming from sister offices, leading to limited staff control, missed deadlines, and poor budgetary discipline.

4. **Poor personnel assignment**–Excessive hours charged to jobs, inadequate experience of personnel, and unkept promises for work delivery are all continuing problems.

5. **Poor cooperation among offices**–Development of similar areas of expertise in sister offices creates competition. The goal should be to share resources rather than to fight for the same projects.

Solutions

Despite such problems, the firm succeeded when it began making improvements in these areas:

- **Communication**–Assign discrete, well-defined tasks to qualified personnel. A task management plan such as the one below would help with this problem.

- **Treatment of sister offices**–Commitment to project tasks and shared responsibilities is a must. Don't take on work if you can't complete it in the given time.

- **Personnel assignments**–When project team members can select the people with whom they work, their chances for success grow. Also: development of a comprehensive inventory of personnel resources is a key element.

- **Planning**–Staff training should include the work sharing experience. Assigning new staff to other offices is good for both staff and firm, and it helps the firm prepare for times when sharing is necessary. The "parent/child" concept should also prevail: larger, better-equipped branches should support smaller branch offices.

- **Distribution of risks and rewards**–The approach to revenue sharing should be uniform and consistently applied. If the supplier office gets the project multiplier, it should foot the bill for other direct costs (ODCs); if the supplier office gets only the interoffice multiplier, the host office should pick up the ODCs.

Critical Findings

The firm's study recommended communicating about quality, budget, and schedule at the beginning of any work sharing project. It also revealed that each branch—large or small—should plan its staffing to best meet its operational needs.

Finally, it affirmed the importance of providing a contracting office with the same quality you would a client. "Since quality means meeting the client's requirements," the report states, "the requirements must be clear and the pathway to meeting them established."

Staff Planning Sheet

Date:_____Project office:_____

Project manager:_____Project number:_____

Scope of work to be performed:_____
_____
_____

<u>Qualifications necessary for person performing task</u>

1. Education/training qualifications:_____
_____

2. Specific technical experience:_____
_____

Level of expertise (senior, midlevel, junior, etc.):_____

3. Task milestones and schedules:_____
_____

4. Task budget:
    _____ Labor hours at _____Labor category

5. Method of sharing revenue/costs:_____

6. Method of project budget and schedule control:
    _____ Weekly (or other) telephone calls from PM to staff
    _____ Weekly (or other) submittals of work product by staff to PM
    _____ Weekly (or other) memo about work progress by staff to PM
    _____ Other _____

CHAPTER 7

MANAGING CLIENT EXPECTATIONS

Involve the Client in Project Startup

After conducting an internal kickoff meeting with the project team, it is important that you schedule a separate kickoff meeting with the client. This will develop the client relationship; the client is an important part of the project and a startup meeting is vital.

- Identify the client's spokesperson(s) by name. Clarification at the start will save uncertainty and potential embarrassment during the project.

- Identify the primary and backup contact at your firm. Make sure the client knows the names of the people he or she should contact at your firm.

- Describe the project team, its members, and their qualifications. Make sure the client understands who is filling each key role.

- Review the project schedule. Point out the key delivery dates, as well as dates of meetings, presentations, and anything that the client must support or might want to attend.

- Review the project payment plan. Ensure that the payment schedule meets the client's expectations and ability to obtain necessary funds as required by the contract terms.

- Provide an outline of near-term project events. The objective is to shape the client's initial expectations and create some sense of excitement about getting the project started.

- Discuss any initial data the project needs. The actual request for data should be submitted in writing, but it is good to discuss this at the meeting.

- Discuss communication plans. Establish a set time each week for conference calls with the client.

- Set a schedule for the remaining project meetings. If it is not possible to set up all the meetings, schedule at least the next three or four, and as each is held, add another to the schedule.

What Clients Expect From Project Managers

The following five traits ranked highest in a survey of 251 clients who were asked which train was most important when choosing a project manager.

1. **World expert at a project type.** Clients expect that the individual running their project has

significant experience running similar projects. Clients are frustrated when their PM is getting on-the-job training for a new project type.

2. **Full authority to get the job done.** Clients often ask that principals be project managers on their projects. The reason? Clients want the individual running their project to have the full authority within their firm to accomplish the project schedule and budget requirements. They are frustrated when PMs must continually seek approval before acting on their behalf.

3. **Ability to communicate well.** Clients want managers who can stand up and make presentations that are persuasive and informative. They are frustrated by individuals with strong technical capability who can't stand before a group and communicate clearly.

4. **Ability to manage the team.** Clients want individuals who can coordinate the activities of their own staff in concert with the staff of the client and any outside agency personnel.

5. **Acceptance of responsibility for the project.** Clients want single point responsibility for the scope of work on the project. They are tired of being referred to a variety of individuals in a small firm on issues as simple as an explanation of an invoice.

The Four "R's" of Superior Client Service

Reachability

This is a coined word referring to how easy it is for the client to contact you. When your client has a problem or question, you can assume that he want to be able to reach you immediately. That isn't always possible, but there are steps you can take to increase your reachability. These include regularly updating your voice mail greeting to include your whereabouts, always letting the receptionist know where you can be reached, and assigning a backup to field client questions when you are unavailable.

Responsiveness.

This is your willingness to adapt to meet client needs. Most technical consulting firms work hard at being responsive. They readily agree to scope changes, alter schedules and shift resources, and put in long hours to accommodate their clients.

Reliability.

This is the quality of trustworthiness that you demonstrate to your clients. Do you consistently meet their requirements and expectations? Do you always follow through with commitments? Without this, you can never be a consistent provider of client service.

Recovery.

Not matter how diligent you are, you will occasionally experience a service breakdown. Recovery relates to the actions you take in such situations to make things right again. A well executed recovery can actually strengthen the relationship with your client.

Make Feedback Part of the Communication Process

Clients are increasingly implementing internal audits of a consultant's work. These audits measure a project manager's willingness to challenge past practices. Fundamental to that process is communication.

For a successful project, your ability to listen to clients is just as important as your experience. Clients think project managers step into a project with preconceived notions, ready to execute what they have already planned in their mind. They don't listen, they don't communicate well, and they're not going to be able to challenge those past practices when they get involved in a project. Part and parcel that the owner owes to that communication process is feedback.

Higher Client Expectations

What clients are really looking for in their team is a way to fight capital costs. A CEO of a major health care facility offered this viewpoint: "We have to look at ways to lower costs. I know that the demands on these facilities are increasing, which drives costs up, so it my goal is to get 10 percent out of the job. I know I must take calculated risks. I'm looking for people who have the experience, and who will come in and challenge us to do things differently."

Clients are investing heavily in these audits and database information to track costs and performance of people on the job. They are looking at all the changes in a project to see if they are design driven, team driven, owner driven, or project management driven. Their mantra is, "If it gets measured, it gets done." So at the end of the job, it's feedback to everybody on the team.

The CEO continued: "We have to tell them that we spent five percent on redesigned items that were not client-directed; that at the end of the job we were not code compliant in certain areas, and we have had to come back to correct certain items. That's an unacceptable level. We have to change that.

"So the challenge for the team is to buy into that idea, to take a risk, and to recognize that there are going to be shortfalls in certain areas, but identify them and correct them, and know that we as clients are looking for people who are willing to take those risks."

The savvy will look at everyone who is a partner in the team. They may have selected the best firm in the world, but if they were given a bad project manager, they will throw up a red flag. In design firms, it's the individuals on the team that count. "If we demand that our consultants assign top people, and only give them an isolated one-time job, we're not making a long-term buying commitment," says one client. "If the designer looks at it as just one job, their commitment to learn the institution's needs and requirements is not going to be cost effective. But if they have the understanding that we're going to do this repetitively, then the investment becomes worthwhile. Then we can reasonably demand a commitment of senior people.

"The capital constraints make it all the more important to do this, so we want to partner with firms who have a portfolio of working with the institution. That firm will have a singular relationship with us, and when we plan a project that firm will be a partner in taking our strategic plan to a facility master plan."

Solutions to the Five Biggest Client Problems

Client service breakdowns among A/E firms follow some consistent patterns. Here's a list of the five most commonly observed problems:

1. **Inadequate communication**. This is the most common cause for service breakdowns. It involves clients, PMs, team members, subcontractors, and other project stakeholders. It results in mistakes, delays, budget overruns, misunderstandings, and lost clients. Improving communication is the best place to start improving client service.

2. **Unclear client service goals**. This problem starts when you fail to adequately uncover client needs. It is further complicated when PMs fail to

properly communicate information to the team. Make sure you sit down with the client at the start of the project and identify expectations.

3. **Project team staffing changes.** Project teams that stay together through the duration of the project typically perform better than those subjected to constant staffing changes. Of course, these changes are often necessary to best allocate firm resources and maintain utilization. In this case, problems can be minimized by frequent team communication and a formal "handoff" process.

4. **Failure to keep internal deadlines.** This routinely leads to a frenzied, last-minute push to get deliverables out the door to meet client deadlines, often at the cost of quality and harmony among coworkers. Service-driven firms display discipline not only in meeting external milestones, but in keeping internal commitments to the team.

5. **Poorly defined standard processes or work products.** Lack of consistent work processes and products result in variable quality and inefficiency. Many firms resist standardization, feeling it impedes creativity and ignores the unique characteristics of each project assignment. But in fact, well-designed standard processes free up resources needed to unleash creativity and client-specific focus.

Clients Sound Off About Switching PMs on the Job

If you make a presentation and introduce Joe as your engineering PM, and six months from now Joe is gone, what impact does that have? We asked five clients for their views.

They are:

Public Client 1 (Sr VP and chief engineer, transit)

Public Client 2 (Chief engineer, transportation authority)

Public Client 3 (VP engineering, construction & regulatory affairs, sports authority)

Private Client 1 (partner, architectural

Private Client 2 (managing director, project development services)

Public Client 1 "It's deadly. You don't want to switch PMs. The most valuable thing you can do on a job is perform well for possible repeat business. Changeover of staff is considered very poor business.

"One thing I look for in a consultant is partnering, but I still expect everybody to put the project first. It's been my experience that all you need is to have one component fail: a sub, an owner, or a contractor. If one group tanks it, everybody else has got to jump in and hold that job up. Even if we fail, I expect your project manager to come in and make it a success. If the job goes down, everybody goes down with it. It may not be your fault, but if it's a bad project, everyone associated with it looks bad. I'm looking for a consultant who, time and time again, makes sure that the job is successful to everybody's taste.

Public Client 2 "It's almost a dishonest presentation: a bait and switch. The selection might have been made solely on the basis of the people you presented for the project."

Public Client 3 "It's very important that the team that comes in and presents is the team we're going to get. That is very critical to us."

Private Client 1 "It's something that we try to avoid. Not only because it's not perceived well by the client, but it negatively affects the project. We will have large jobs that take a long time to finish—sometimes 7 to 8 years—but halfway through the project, nobody on the design team is still there. Continuity is critical to a large project, as someone may not know why something was done that way a few years down the road.

"The other side of the coin is the reality of business, and things change, people move on. If something happens, you must be up front with your client and make sure that they have a clear understanding of what is going on, and make sure that they have a voice in any substitution, as these are the key people on a job."

Private Client 2 "Making a team change is a bad thing to do, certainly if it is done early on as a bait-and-switch. But change is inevitable: people quit, they move on, they get sick, etc. The only thing more deadly is taking a person off one job and put them on another job, and we know about it. The bigger issue is how it handled; the worst thing a firm can do is not come to the table and talk about it."

Public Clients Sound Off About Pet Peeves

To public clients, design firms' presentations can get very repetitive, and even overwhelming at times. They all want to give every consultant their due, but every week they may receive 100 letters, 50 cold calls, and numerous emails. It's impossible for them to handle all of it. It's important that you know the actions that turn them off, as well as what makes them listen. Here's a potpourri of pet peeves and helpful comments from public clients.

Pet Peeves

According to some clients, the most obnoxious thing a potential consultant can do is show up at their office demanding a meeting. They dub it an "intervention," and at most times, the client cannot, or will not, accommodate them. Another pet peeve is that some of the marketing people that call on them are not as knowledgeable about the profession as they are in communications. "It has to be substance, or it becomes a dance of communications," one client maintains.

References are Critical

Clients make extensive use of references and background checks, and draw upon sister agencies to do this. Have you ever had clients call your reference and find out that the contact has moved on, or worse, given you a bad reference? Clients all have. Their advice: "Check your own references, and make sure the phone numbers are current."

Joint Ventures are Tricky

When a national firm with a signature designer and a local firm join together on a project, the team isn't always coordinated. One client commented: "I have had to introduce the lead designer to the project manager for the first time at the interview. You should be coordinated, but you don't have to rehearse it to the point of a stage production."

Is LEED an Important Criteria?

Said one client, "All of our projects must be certified. Under the LEED system, our goal is 'silver.' The lead designer should also have LEED experience, and be included in your portfolio in dealing with sustainability."

On Proposals

"We want to know whether you care if we are your client or not," explained one client. "The person reading the proposal can easily pick the firms who really put care into them, as they stick out from the rest, and the ones that are boilerplate, well, you can spot them in an instant."

On Site Visits

"The people who came to the site and took photos, went to our Website and found out what we were doing, walked around, or called and asked questions, usually came up with something useful that differentiated them from the crowd."

On Interviews

"I'll grant a firm an interview, and ask 'what strengths distinguish you from the other firms?' People who say they can do everything won't be remembered. You have to make your firm different. You have to figure out some specific aspect of the job that will make you stand out, such as knowing the date of commencement at an educational setting, because you shouldn't be working on a site on the project on that day. Little things like that work in your favor."

A Threshold of Pain?

"We select bright, capable people. We've moved away from wanting to see exact experience in a project type. We're also looking for a threshold of pain that is qualitative. Who are you giving up for our project? Often, we will get whoever is available, as opposed to who is the best person.

On Experience

"We select on experience, but also on the firm's capacity for complexity. Personalities are also a major factor. We look very closely at who the firm proposes as PM and PIC, and we are not shy about saying 'We like your team, we like your work, but we need the other partner to be involved.'"

About the Project Manager

"It's really important to know the agency to which you are proposing. You need to know the personality of the organization. You need to know who the client's PM is, how the selection process works, and the makeup of the organization." A small engineering firm recently won a major project over five formidable larger firms because the small firm offered a senior VP as project manager on the project, since their research showed that this was the level of involvement and commitment that the client wanted and expected.

How to Plan for Contract Modifications

At the outset of every project, you and your client should mutually agree on how to handle potential changes to your scope of services that will affect the schedule and budget. At the project kickoff meeting, resolve the following issues regarding any changes:

- What kind of notification is required?
- What is the basis for estimating extra costs?
- Whose approval is required?
- How long should the approval process take?

- What should be done while awaiting approval?

Addressing these items before the need arises has two major client relations benefits. First, it establishes in the client's mind the possibility that changes may become necessary. When they do, it isn't a total surprise. Second, it avoids procedural problems from disrupting discussions related to the merit of a particular request for a contract charge.

Eight Ways to Keep Your Clients

1. Know your clients' business. When vendors, consultants and contractors asked the president of Intel how they can get more work from the giant computer chip manufacturer, he told them: "Go out and learn how to make chips. Then come back and help us do it better."

2. At regular intervals throughout the project, send a handwritten note thanking the client for their assistance. Let them know how smoothly the project is going because of their dedication to the schedule.

3. Copy the client on project correspondence. Keep them informed of activity with approval agencies, subs, vendors, and suppliers. It means more paper or a fuller email inbox, but the client will love it.

4. When asked to quote hourly rates in a proposal, don't give precise dollar figures. Instead, quote a range of rates for each staff level. This allows you

to adjust later and prevents clients from adding up hours and taking issue with your invoices.

5. When scope is hard to define, provide the client with a menu of "mini-scoped" work bundles from which to select. Each work bundle clearly defines the work it covers (and doesn't cover) and is accompanied by a lump sum fee range.

6. Identify the "hot buttons," those issues which are driving the project and on which the success of the job will turn. When writing your proposal, everything must relate back to those issues.

7. Call your customer even if you have nothing to report. Let them know you are working steadily and everything is going smoothly.

8. When preparing proposals or presentations, list the top ten possible objections that a client may have to hiring you. (You're too big, small, old, young, far away, etc.) Then devise strategies that turn those objections into advantages for the client. (Yes, our firm is small. We keep it that way so we can provide you with the fast-response service you demand.)

Weekly Progress Reports Create Long-Term Clients

One of the best tools for delivering client satisfaction is a simple, one-page weekly project status report. While this may seem excessive to those who send a progress report once a month, we have found that it is better to deliver small reports more often than to send larger reports less often. Here's how you do it:

- Gather input from the project team on Friday to send to the client on Monday. The whole process should not take more than 20 minutes.

- Cover what you accomplished for the week and what you will work on the following week, and list any scope or schedule changes. Mention any input you may need from the client.

- Boil your report down to the most important information. It should fit on one piece of paper.

There are a few cautions that come with this method:

1. Don't repeat the same content every week. This shows indifference to the client, and he or she will start to ignore the reports.

2. Don't show bad news every week. It's okay to report that you are behind schedule, but reporting that you are behind week after week will build a negative impression of your firm.

3. Don't be inconsistent with the frequency of your reports. If it is too difficult to deliver weekly reports on every project, choose a few projects to report on weekly, and choose a few to report on every other week.

Firms who use weekly progress reports have seen an overwhelmingly positive response from clients. Most save the reports electronically, and one client puts his company header on top of the reports and sends them to his boss.

Six Essentials for Getting Paid on Time

As project manager, it's up to you to make sure your firm is getting paid for its services. Develop a simple regimen of getting invoices out and getting paid by following these steps:

1. Begin by discussing invoice format and frequency with the client at the beginning of the project. Tell the client what to expect, and customize invoices to client needs and desires.

2. Develop a billing and payment schedule for the full duration of the project. Use the schedule to allow the client to alert bookkeeping and accounting staff, as well as to plan cash flow.

3. Submit invoices at least monthly (biweekly if acceptable to the client). Submit invoices on a specific date each month. Clients will then get into the habit of receiving—and paying—invoices regularly.

4. Submit invoices as quickly as possible after interim work or tasks are complete. Bill while your work effort is fresh in the client's memory. The longer you wait, the more questions you will have to answer in order to get paid.

5. Match your billing cycle with the client's billing or payment cycle. Don't use your accounting department's schedule, use the client's.

6. Invoice separately for additional services and reimbursables. Don't let a dispute over a minor or separate item hold up all other payments or services that are due.

Brainstorm Ways to Impress Your Clients

When planning every project, ask yourself, "What am I going to do to blow the client away?" Make a list of possible service opportunities as part of your client care plan.

Here are some examples:

Develop a Project Management Plan

Manage files for clients

Train client staff

Provide a service guarantee

Deliver meeting summaries within 24 hours

Maintain accessibility

Allow for no surprises

Offer progress reporting

Conduct lessons learned

Provide a client feedback survey

Set a kickoff meeting

Create measured responsiveness

Develop a team directory

Return calls within the same day

Offer budget forecasting

Provide over-the-shoulder reviews

Develop a communications plan

Implement a QC plan

Conduct project follow-up

Perform client "touches"

The "Perfect Client"

Even the "perfect client" has unique opinions and expectations (which he/she may not be aware of consciously—until the consultant can figure them out and state them better than the client has done). Naturally, the ideal client will expect the work product to meet these expectations, expressed or not.

The perfect client is one who:

- Writes a good RFP.

- Treats proposers fairly—but may give an "unfair" advantage to consultant(s) who have (1) developed a relationship with them, (2) expressed interest in their project early on, and (3) demonstrated that they've got the experience to conduct the project.

- Has control over the purchasing department (and thus does not place a high priority on price).

- Has control over the contracts department (and therefore agrees to equitable terms).

- Devotes enough time to understand the project so as to be able to clearly express his/her expectations.

- Controls the interactions of his/her organization with the members of the consultant's team.

16 Ways to Keep Your Clients

1. Set up a toll-free "800" trouble-shooting hot-line for clients to use once a project is finished. Encourage them to call with any questions or problems.

2. Appoint a senior member of your team as your client ombudsman. Tell clients that this person is always available to lend an ear when things aren't going well, or to pass on a message they may be hard put to deliver in person.

3. Always reinforce written communications (including e-mails) with a telephone (or in-person) follow-up. A missed message could mean a missed opportunity.

4. Provide your client with your home phone number. It sends a message that your service surpasses normal levels. Few will abuse the

privilege; most will use it only in an emergency (as you would want them to anyway).

5. Provide a contract clause that guarantees you will return phone calls within four hours. If you fail to live up to the promise, the client gets a $100 invoice reduction (or dinner for two, etc.)

6. Verbal communication is a two-way street. As a receiver, you can help by actively listening, using your eyes and facial expressions to show interest, and asking questions for clarification.

7. Provide all project managers with cell phones so they can be reached when out of the office. Other service businesses (doctors, real estate agents, construction professionals) use them. Why not A/Es?

8. When browsing newspapers, magazines, or newsletters, watch for articles that apply to your client's business. Clip and send them to the client with a hand-written note saying, "Thought you might be interested...."

9. Set up a "Frequent Client Program" that rewards clients who return with repeat or referral work. For every $10,000 dollars in fee they spend, give them a free day of consulting, a certificate worth $1,000 off their next project, four front row tickets to the ball game/symphony/auto race, etc.

10. Provide a seminar to your client's staff or customers shortly after project kickoff. The half-day session will cover all aspects of the project, the background, design philosophy, technology

involved, and project process. Hold update sessions as the project progresses.

11. Give a seminar to the client's staff in a specialty area—CAD translation, equipment operation, etc. Tap the talent you have in-house and apply your creativity.

12. At the beginning of the project, set up a phone call schedule with your client. Decide, for example, that every Thursday at 2:30 p.m. you will call the client and update him or her on project progress. This is also a time- management aid; it helps the client resist calling you whenever there is a problem. If it's Wednesday afternoon, he or she will likely "wait until tomorrow."

13. Sponsor a prize or trophy for your client's in-house bowling league.

14. Patronize your client's products or services. If your client is PepsiCo, don't serve Coke during project meetings.

15. At project start-up, sit with your customer and design a "report card" on which they will mark your performance at regular intervals. Establish and rank whatever criteria they feel to be most important. Sit together to discuss your interim "grades," then wrap up with "finals" at project close-out. Besides communicating a commitment to service and quality, this practice keeps your staff sensitive to the unique requirements of the project.

16. Invite half a dozen clients to a focus group lunch where they can discuss their issues. Find out what concerns them in their day-to-day problems and struggles. Learn how you can deliver better service and become more of a "partner" in their operations.

Be Proactive in Your Client Communications

Virtually all communications between the client and the A/E/C firms are initiated because one of the parties needs something from the other. Such communications are always reactive and often negative.

The best that can be hoped for is that each person is reasonably responsive to the needs of the others. But often the price of responsiveness is interrupting other previously planned activities.

Client communications can be improved significantly by being proactive rather than reactive. Each project should have an agreed upon communications plan including written progress reports, meetings and phone calls.

Written Progress Reports

Whether required by contract or not, you, as project manager, should submit progress reports to the client on a regularly scheduled basis (such as "every Monday" or "by the 5th of every month"). The contents should also be agreed upon with the client, including such items as:

Summary of work done last period

Forecast of activities during the next period

Changes in scope made last period

Budget status

Schedule status

Input required from the client

Other problems

Meetings

In addition to written updates, it is often useful for the client and the PM to plan regular meetings to discuss the status of the project and resolve any problems that may have arisen. It is important that such meetings be held on the same day, at the same time, and in the same place. For example, the agreement may be for a meeting every Friday at 10:30 a.m. at the design firm's office. The agenda of such regularly scheduled meetings can be similar to the items described above for written progress reports.

Phone calls

When regular meetings are considered impractical or where there are long-time intervals between such meetings, regularly scheduled phone calls can effectively fill in the gaps. Again, it is essential that these calls be scheduled for the same time and day (e.g., every Tuesday at 9 a.m.).

Measuring Conformance

Developing a client communications plan, then failing to follow it, is worse than having no plan at all. Such failure to follow through with a commitment can seriously damage your firm's credibility. Nonconformance must therefore be measured to ensure that appropriate actions are taken to eliminate problems before they arise.

One way to accomplish this measurement is to ensure that your project secretary receives copies of written reports, meeting minutes, and notes of telephone conversations. Once a month, these can be tallied and compared to the requirements for all the projects for which the secretary is responsible.

Four PM Status Activities You Should Do For Your Client Every Week

You should communicate with the client at least weekly to apprise them of the team's status and key issues. In return, make sure to request any current, relevant information the client may have. If you cannot meet the client in person, fax, email, or mail a simple project status report.

In addition, you should:

- Review labor costs and staff hour reports from accounting.

- Ensure that authorized staff is working on the job, that hourly charges are correct, and that people are working on their scheduled tasks.

- Determine that the charged hours are reasonable and within the budget for the associated work. If not, take corrective action.

- Resolve time-charge errors with both the individual involved and the accounting department.

- Hold weekly project meetings to keep all team members apprised of the overall status of the project.

- Schedule these meetings to occur on the same day and time each week. The complexity of the project and level of activity on the project will determine how detailed the meeting must be.

- Develop, publish and distribute ahead of time an agenda, so team members can be prepared for the meeting.

Five Ways to Exceed Client Expectations

Here are 5 important tips on managing client and staff expectations

1. **See your service through the client's eyes.** When you learn the potential problems your client will find with your service, you understand what you need to convey to them.

2. **Make communications with clients more clear.** Leaving room for your clients to interpret what you say opens the door for disappointment.

3. **Reinforce client expectations often.** Budget time in client meetings to reiterate exactly what you are going to do. Find more than one way to explain what you are going to do. Look for a "tell

sign" from the client so you know when they "get it."

4. **Get credit from clients for putting out extra effort.** If you set up realistic goals with your clients—and exceed them—you will collect goodwill from them every time.

5. **Foster a culture of long-term satisfaction.** When you manage client expectations effecttively, you establish a culture of satisfaction. This means ensuring the client understands what's going to happen and when, and following through. These kinds of relationships are hard to build but are extremely valuable in getting repeat business and referrals.

Avoid the "Bait and Switch" Approach to Client Management

If there is one thing clients hate, it is when they see new people taking over their projects. Repeat clients often want assurance that a certain person, usually a principal, will be involved in their projects.

The "bait and switch" method of simply rotating staff from principal to project manager can easily upset a client and kill any chances of future work. So how do you successfully take over on a project when a principal built the relationship with the client and won the job?

The key is through developing a transitional or "courting" period, where you join the principal at client meetings, so you can tackle relationship-building together.

If the client sees you early on, he or she will establish confidence in you, while the principal can slowly phases out of the picture. The principal may go to an occasional meeting but should not completely disappear from the project. This transition takes time. Depending on the client, it may even take up to a year.

In addition, you must show some humility and give credit to your principal, even when he or she is not present. If your client expects a certain person to stay involved on the project, let the client know that you have discussed, giving extra assurance to your client.

Preparing a Client Service Plan

A good plan provides direction for the project team on how specific service deliverables will be handled throughout the project. Preparing this plan recognizes that client service involves time and expense, and should be managed accordingly.

- **Client communications**
  - Frequency and method of routine communications
  - Project status reporting
- **Meeting with client**
  - Number/timing of meetings

- Responsibility for planning and facilitating meetings

- **Decisions and involvement**

  - Client involvement in decisions and team meetings
  - Client approvals of draft deliverables (when? by whom?)

- **Information and data**

  - Information to be routinely reported to client and format
  - Record keeping for client purposes
  - Data access or sharing with client

- **Deliverable standards**

  - Format for reports and construction documents
  - Document control procedures

- **Invoicing and payment**

  - Invoice format and timing
  - Special payment arrangements

- **Changes**

  - Management
  - Basis for estimating extra costs
  - Response to mistakes

- **Performance feedback**

  - Best method of obtaining feedback from the client.

Six Tips for Enhancing Cash Flow

One senior PM from a Midwest firm targets 30 days for invoice turnaround. He developed the following simple regimen for getting invoices out and getting paid fast:

1. Begin by discussing invoice format and frequency with the client at the beginning of the project. Tell the client what to expect, and customize invoices to the client's needs.

2. Develop a billing and payment schedule for the full duration of the project. Use the schedule to allow the client to alert accounting staff, as well as to plan cash flow.

3. Submit invoices at least monthly, or bi-weekly if acceptable to the client. Submit invoices on a specific date each month—do not miss the monthly deadline.

4. Submit all invoices as quickly as possible after interim work or tasks are complete. Bill while your work effort is fresh in the client's memory. The longer you wait, the more questions you'll have to answer to get paid.

5. Match your billing cycle with the client's billing or payment cycle. Don't use your accounting department's schedule—use the client's.

6. Invoice separately for basic services professional fees, additional services professional fees, and reimbursable expenses. Don't let a dispute over a minor or separate item hold up all valid payments due.

Call for Payment—Your Clients Will Thank You

Your clients want you to ask for payment. Why? They need to tell you what they're thinking about the project—about what's bothering them and what they want you to do better. They want to tell you what they *really* want.

This is hard for clients. Nobody likes saying, "I don't like how you did this. You fouled up!" But in a construction project where careers and corporations depend on the outcome, success hinges on 100 percent honest communication.

Airing of Grievances

A good way to elicit honesty from clients is to ask for payment when it is late. It's not enough to send the invoice; clients actually need you to call them. Asking for payment will give them the chance to say what they're thinking.

It happens like this: your client is displeased about some facet of the project. He or she gets the invoice, and then won't pay it because you're not delivering what was requested: you haven't earned your fee. But the client won't call and confront you; it's easier to just "stew." After all, it's money in the client's bank.

You can give them the chance—by reminding them that payment is late. Then they'll say, "Well, I've got a few things I need to talk about." Let them talk, let them know you've heard, and reach agreement on how you will fix any problems.

Asking for a Referral? Not So Fast!

You have won the project and have just begun working with the client, who seems pleased with your work. You now wonder if the client knows of others who may need your service. After all, in the days before the sophisticated marketing strategies of today, most firms relied mainly on tips and referrals as their mainstay for getting new work. It was important for the principals to foster relationships that would keep them in contact with their client network, or there wouldn't be any new work coming in.

Referrals are still one of the best forms of marketing. However, you will find that asking for a referral before it's appropriate may not be the wisest choice. It puts the client in an uncomfortable position. Until they reach the point that they are totally satisfied with your performance, they are certainly not going to recommend your firm to others without feeling used.

Looking at the other side of the coin, how well does the client know you so early in the process? They may appear to be excellent contacts, but they are not regular clients yet. They must be nurtured in a gradual manner. Even though you have cut out the bulk of the front-end marketing work and accompanying expense, there is still a lot of relationship-building work ahead.

Timing Is Everything

One solution for shortening this effort comes from marketing expert John Graham of Graham

Communications, and author of *The New Magnet Marketing* and *Break The Rules Selling.* Graham recommends using the "prospects contact letter." The letter includes the person who gave you their name, the length of time the person has been a client of the firm, and how you are helping them on their project. The letter then indicates that you will be staying in touch with them regularly, but invite them to contact you anytime if they have a specific or immediate need.

Then, contact the client when the work is nearly completed, with the following statement: "Our firm wants you to be completely satisfied with our service. I recognize that this takes time. Some months from now, I will ask you for suggestions for those who might benefit from receiving our newsletter, or other information. Our approach is to give them an opportunity to get acquainted with what we do and how we work before contacting them."

This carefully timed approach will yield much greater results, not only from those new contacts who should be your fast-track to new work, but from the satisfied client, who may already be contemplating add-on work for you, or perhaps even a new project.

Here is a typical comment gleaned from an interview with just such a satisfied bank client:

"They were always on call and always responded at those times that I needed to meet, which didn't fit the typical 8 to 5 schedule. There's a major remodeling job coming up, and I didn't even go to another architectural firm, because I have a tremendous comfort zone in their ability to get that job done."

How to Define Your Clients' Critical Success Factors?

One of your first goals on a project is to understand your client's priorities. Unfortunately, clients are not always skilled at communicating their goals and needs. In this case, you need to do some "hand holding" and work with them to create measurable goals for the project.

Your best approach is to create a list of critical success factors for the project. Critical success factors are those elements of the project that you absolutely must accomplish to reach the client's vision. Your objective is to define those factors and then assign quantifiable performance measures for each factor.

The following are some examples of critical success factors required by clients, followed by performance measures that clarify each factor.

Critical Success Factors

1. Attractive Building
2. Highly automated
3. Adequate parking
4. Reasonable cost
5. Minimal change orders

Performance Measures

1. Approved by committee
2. Operated by six people
3. Parking for 45 cars
4. Cost < $100/square foot
5. Change orders < $70,000

The Client Sponsor

An all-too-common problem in client relations occurs when a project manager is unable to cope with a client who is becoming dissatisfied with the firm's work. This can result from the PM failing to recognize subtle signs of client dissatisfaction. Or it may be that the project manager knows there is a problem but, for whatever reason, fails to request help from the firm's senior managers.

A solution to this problem is the assignment of a client sponsor for each project. The client sponsor should be a senior manager who:

- Keeps in touch with the client from time to time, assuring that the client remains well satisfied with the firm's services

- Acts as an in-house advocate for the client, assuring that the project receives the appropriate priority within the office.

- Serves as a point of contact when the client has a problem that he or she does not wish to discuss with the PM.

- Obtains informal and formal performance evaluation upon completion of the project.

- Keeps in touch with the client periodically as a way of identifying potential future projects.

A recommended procedure for implementing a client sponsor program:

A client sponsor is selected for each client. The client sponsor keeps in touch with the client periodically to assure his/her total satisfaction. During project execution, the client sponsor takes whatever measures are necessary to correct any client relations problems.

Upon completion of the project, the client sponsor calls or visits the client to obtain an informal debriefing the firm's performance and asks the client to fill out an evaluation form. If the client was satisfied, the client sponsor should also inquire about future projects in which the firm may be involved.

The client evaluation forms are given a numerical value based on the following:

4 points – exceeded expectations

3 points – met expectations

2 points – needs improvement

1 point – serious problem

A point can be plotted for each project, based on the completion date and overall assessment ranking of each project. These data will provide a quantitative measure of client satisfaction

After collecting data for a year, bar charts can be developed showing the overall ranking of the firm's performance as well as the average ranking for each evaluation category. This data can be used to prioritize areas that need the most improvement.

In implementing a client sponsor program, it is imperative that the firm's client sponsor and project manager work as a team. This required open communications in which all contacts with the client are discussed frankly and objectively. If the project manager feels that he/she is being subverted, rather than assisted, by the client sponsor, the client will quickly observe this friction and the program will be counterproductive.

Both the client sponsor and the project manager must focus on a single common objective—total client satisfaction—and all personal goals must be subordinated when they deviate from this objective.

Sacrificing Short-term Gains

A prevalent fear among clients is that design firms tend to increase a project's size and complexity in order to increase their fees. Unfortunately, there have been many cases where such fears were well founded and, as a result, most sophisticated clients will enter into professional service contracts with one hand firmly on their wallet. This lack of trust causes stress between the design professional and the client whenever the scope of work is altered during the course of the project, and produces an unhappy ending to many projects that at first appeared very promising.

Managers in professional service firms must be sensitive to this built-in distrust among clients and should go out of their way to allay these concerns. The client's interests must be placed above the short-term interests of the design firm—and the client must know that the design firm has the client's interests as its first priority.

Five Ways to Lose Your Clients

Here are five common mistakes that make design firm clients want to say "adios."

1. **Not keeping in regular contact.** At all costs, you must keep your clients in the loop. Schedule regular conference calls with them. Have their team meet with your team. If you avoid their input, then your clients could go their own way.

2. **Not being creative.** Being creative means understanding the client's long-term business strategy, then finding innovative designs to support that strategy. If you fail to learn about your client's business—if you assume he or she will hire you just because "you've done this same kind of project before"—then you might not be doing it again.

3. **Negativity.** Clients want you to go the extra mile. That could mean representing them at city council or school board meetings. It could mean attending conferences in their industry. If you resist going the distance for them, your client could become distant.

4. **Being disrespectful.** Your client is the expert in his or her business, and that is the business you are "building." It may be true that you know more about design, but your client is not interested so much in design as in business growth. Question or discount the client's expertise, and you are shooting yourself in the foot.

5. **Not delegating.** Your firm's value equals the total intellectual capital of all your staff members. By withdrawing some of that "capital" from the transaction, you cheat your client and fail to deliver your best product. Clients who get the next best may not be so quick to come back.

Troubleshooting: The High Cost of Hidden Expectations

The last thing your client wants is surprises, especially near the end of a project. A recent case history makes this point in stark terms:

An engineer was asked to perform tests and develop a preliminary design for a new septic system to replace a failed system for a school. Initial investigations indicated that there were several possible sites, including one on the athletic fields, and another on an adjacent hill.

After preliminary testing, the engineer told the school board overseeing the work that the hill was a feasible—but difficult—site. The school committee agreed to place the field on the side of the hill, despite its higher costs, to avoid interrupting activities on the athletic fields.

The town approved the committee's request for funds, and a subsequent vote confirmed the approval. Everyone anticipated that the project would go ahead smoothly.

Imagine the school committee's surprise when, some time later, the engineer announced that the place on the hill required state approval—and that such approval was unlikely. Further, the engineer indicated that additional testing would be necessary to design the hill system.

The committee was furious, believing that it had been misled. Also, because the committee had presented the hill option to the Town and had received funding approval based on the fact the playing fields would be operational during construction, the committee felt that its integrity was at risk. With considerable acrimony, the engineer was terminated.

The Moral

On all design projects keep these crucial issues in mind:

- Be very careful when making statements that affect a client's hidden agenda. Sometimes the unexpressed needs of a client are more important than the stated requirements. In this case, the main objective of the school committee was to design a system that would allow continued use of the athletic fields. Cost and operational efficiency were secondary.

- Check with all applicable authorities before making procedural statements of fact. A simple call to the State DEP would have revealed that a variance was needed to use the slower percolation on the hillside vs. the athletic field, and that such a variance would be difficult or impossible to obtain.

- Keep your client informed of risk factors at all times. Document any changed conditions—including increased cost, time delays, possible permit problems, or potential operational difficulties that alter the risk factors.

Use Caution when Switching PMs

One of the worst things your firm can do is switch project managers in the middle of a project. This is a major pet peeve with clients, so avoid it if at all possible. However, when switching PMs is unavoidable, follow these steps:

- Assign an alternate from the beginning. This tells the client you are ready for every contingency.

- Switch to a principal. This will "soften the blow" with clients. Explain that "we felt your project warranted the extra experience a principal could provide." They may even see it as an advantage.

Remember, it's always better to switch up, not down.

- Let the client help in the decision process. Solicit his or her input, and develop a plan to address concerns.

- Start early. A transition that appears planned and managed is much more acceptable to a client than one that seems reactive.

- Assign at least a full day for information transfer. Don't rush the process. Plan sufficient time for you and the other PM to go over the details of the project.

Handling Client Pushback

One of the toughest things you deal with as a PM is handling pushback from your clients. When you handle client pushback well, the toughest problems on a project (even problems that are a result of your mistake) can be overcome with no damage to your relationship with your client.

If you don't deal effectively with client pushback, you can trash a client relationship—even if the problem is minor and not your fault. This is huge because not only are you less likely to get additional work from your client, you can kiss a reference—and perhaps dozens of referrals—goodbye. John Doerr, Principal of the Wellesley Hills Group offers these tips for handling clients' objections effectively:

1. **Treat every client pushback like it has merit.** Your first impulse may be to argue or minimize the pushback as trivial or a waste of your time. Your better option is to:

   - Listen fully to the problem (do not interrupt or anticipate).

   - Ask permission to completely understand the issue (e.g., "let me understand what you are saying").

   - Ask questions and re-state or clarify the issue

   - Choose your response

2. **Remember that responding to pushback often requires a process—not just a verbal answer—to overcome.** Your client is usually just one of several client stakeholders involved with a project. When you take a proactive role in making sure that your solution addresses the complexities of multi-stakeholder scenarios, your client will see you as an advocate and a problem solver.

3. **Don't always take "yes" for an answer.** Take it upon yourself to make absolutely sure that your response to the pushback is the best possible solution.

Breaking Bad News to Clients

When dealing with clients, you need to remember that perception is reality. If your clients perceive that you're looking out for their best interests, they're happy. But this becomes difficult when you have to break bad news to them about their project.

Offer Alternatives.

The best way to communicate bad news is by letting the client make the choice of how to resolve the problem.

For example, if a client asks you to do additional work, and this work will require a schedule extension, first discuss the necessary changes with the client. And then offer one of the following three alternatives:

- Using your current team, you will revise the scope of the work, eliminate some items, and complete the project on schedule.

- You will bring in additional staff from one or more of your branch offices to work on the project. The additional labor will result in an increase in the fee to the client.

- Have the client take on some of the tasks— especially if he/she has in-house technical staff— and in this way the client will avoid a fee increase.

Regardless of which option clients choose, they won't point the finger at you. After all, they made the choice.

Don't Let Cross-selling Opportunities Slip By

As the project manager, you more than anyone else have the ability to find out the needs of your client, and you are in a position to help sell the services of another part of your firm to an existing client. Firms who do not emphasize cross-selling are missing major opportunities. It is ten times harder to sell to a new client. With cross-selling, you already know your client, and you are in the position to make a 'warm' call as opposed to a cold call.

So why don't we cross-sell? There are a number of different barriers that keep these opportunities from happening. Here are several common roadblocks, followed by some strategies to overcome these barriers.

1. **Who gets the credit?** Pursuing a cross-selling opportunity must be a mutual decision between you and the new project manager or contact in the other department of your firm. It is a group effort with group credit.

2. **Risk of failure.** To get the new project manager up to speed, you must spend some time with the person and educate them on the client. This will greatly help your chances of winning over the client.

3. **"What's in it for me?"** You must truly believe that the opportunity is in the best interest of the client organization. By offering an array of services, you become a trusted "advisor" in more ways than one.

4. **One department is not giving enough support for building the cross-sell.** One engineering firm we know gives the cross-selling initiative to an authority above the two people in the different departments to manage to cross-sell opportunity.

This can help the new initiative from "dying from inertia."

Add-On Work Opportunities as You Work

Does your project team regularly create add-on work opportunities? It should. Getting more work from your existing clients is typically the foundation to a firm's marketing program.

Here are a number of ways to make this discovery process a routine act:

1. Set aside time for a client needs assessment to examine what is new, changing, or troublesome in the client's current operations. This should take place at quarterly points during the project's duration or added as an agenda item during weekly internal project team updates.

2. Track the nature and frequency of issues that crop up over the course of the project. Is a trend surfacing? Is one area of the client's operations in greater need of help?

3. Brainstorm with the project team and across project teams to identify strategies that address recurring issues or ideas. Include brainstorming on how to educate team members and the client concerning the issue or idea.

4. Set the best ideas in motion. Include your client in developing the ideas and action plans fully.

5. Compare results across project teams. Determine which strategies appealed to clients and what plan worked best.

Invoicing and Collection Tips

Here's some good advice on making project invoices more effective:

- Use a spreadsheet program to format your invoices—avoid unnecessary math errors.

- Attach a letter with every invoice that summarizes the work done during that period.

- The letter should acknowledge prior payments or if there is a past due amount.

- The letter is a vehicle to inform the client when the project has moved into another phase of work or has incurred additional services.

- The letter can also contain language that indicates if payment is received, then the client acknowledges satisfaction with the services received.

- The principal in charge of invoices should consult with you and review each invoice to determine if the amount being billed is commensurate with the work performed.

- The principal in charge should also keep track of the project during construction administration.

- The majority of lawsuits against design professionals are initiated as countersuits to a design professionals suit for fee collection.

Invoices are your early warning system for averting problems.

Time Is Money—Get Your Bills Out Fast

Even in the best of times, it's easy to let day-to-day tasks slip. And letting your billing slip can cost you profits! Calculating your firm's "Days Work-In-Process" (WIP) shows just how effective you are in getting invoices to clients after you've performed the work. Unbilled WIP are fees for work performed but you haven't yet sent out the invoices.

Here's how to calculate your WIP:

(Unbilled WIP ÷ Total Annual Revenues) x 365 = Days WIP

Most firms have between 25 and 30 days of unbilled revenues. The top firms have reduced this to between 15 and 20 days. Obviously, the fewer WIP days, the better. Clients generally wait for an invoice before they pay you, so the sooner you bill, the sooner you'll receive a check.

PSMJ recommends calculating this ratio for each project manager, as a sudden increase in Days WIP is often the first indication of problems on the job, which could result in contract overruns.

How to Prevent Slow Collections

Looking for an effective collection policy for slow-paying clients? Effective, faster collections begin before you sign a contract—in your project billing processes—not after an invoice is 60 days old.

Firms that have effective pre-contract collection practices follow these procedures. You may want to do likewise.

- **Run a credit check on new clients.** If a credit check is impractical, get bank references. Also get the names of design firms that the new clients may have used before, and check these references.

- **Ask for a retainer.** Clients may say no, but they can't say yes if you don't ask. Another tip: price your proposal with a higher fee if there is no retainer. The lower price may attract more interest in your retainer request.

- **Ask for (and get) clear client information on the invoice approval process, and check issuing processes.** Find out if you can email invoices or receive electronic fund transfers. Making the client aware of the importance you place on getting paid is a crucial first step.

- **Propose contract clauses that stress your collection expectations.** Include clauses regarding interest on late payments, the right to stop work, and favorable (in relation to work effort) billing schedules. If the client does not want these clauses, use a second proposal at a higher price. Use the pre-contract signing period to find out exactly when you will be paid and to try to identify the clients you should say no to before they owe you a sizable amount of money.

Following are the procedures to use once the work starts (don't wait until after the end of the month to invoice):

- Have all lump sum progress billings out of your office by the last Tuesday of the month. If project managers do not know what percentage complete they will be at the end of the current week, maybe they shouldn't be PMs.

- If you make a project milestone delivery to clients during the week, bill it that week. If you have a project checklist (for a 90 percent submittal, say), include on your list the 90 percent invoice going out that day.

- On the first project invoice, confirm (within 5 days of billing) the acceptability of the invoice format and content. Clear up any potential approval problems before you have invoices for 2 months' services outstanding.

Firms that emphasize getting paid before they start work and during the invoicing process are the firms that make the upper quartile in collections.

Want to visualize what being an upper quartile firm would mean for you? Just take your total (gross) revenues for last month and add that amount to your cash. That is what reducing payments due by 30 days will do for your firm. A 30-day improvement is equal to current upper-quartile firm performance. A quarter of all design firms have made this happen. Shouldn't you?

Signs You Won't Get Paid

Watch out for signals which indicate an attempt by clients to slow down their payments to you. These signals may indicate that you won't get paid at all.

- **Checks from remote banks.** National organizations may delay their effective payments to you by paying on remote banks. This delays the time when you can use the money and lengthens the time they can use their money.

- **Postdated checks.** This client obviously does not have your money now and "hopes" he/she will have it when the check becomes valid.

- **Alleged errors in billing.** The time it takes to validate your changes is the time during which the client has money instead of you.

- **Partial payments.** While some money is better than none, partial payments may be a way of delaying your collection efforts while the client uses your money.

- **Lost in mail.** Some firms say that a check is lost in the mail or even deliberately mail the check to the wrong address to delay cashing of the check.

Work to enforce your credit policies. Encourage clients to let you know when they will have difficulty meeting your payment schedules. Be flexible and accommodating in your discussions with them so that they know they can talk to you instead of using these tricks.

In addition, some of the actions below may be helpful in collecting past due accounts:

- Call for a face-to-face meeting. Reiterate your commitment to the project, and get a specific date and offer to send a courier to pick up the check.

- State that you have consultants to pay and cannot jeopardize either the project or your relationship with these consultants by not paying them on time.

  - Write a letter expressing your serious concern, and reiterate the above items. Restate that there was no indication whatsoever that the services were not within expectations. Suggest, "Perhaps we are going too fast" or "Should we temporarily stop if funds are a problem?" Depending on circumstances, a letter may be sent by registered mail, which is a very effective attention-getting device.

The next steps are more drastic. Start with hinting at collection action, then "other avenues." Having a lawyer draft a statement of claim (Without Prejudice) is one possibility to be carefully weighed in terms of its cost-benefit ratio.

How to Collect on Those Overdue Accounts

Listed below are some actions that you might find helpful in collecting past-due accounts.

- Verify that there are no administrative problems with the invoice, such as a wrong format, its being sent to the wrong person, etc.

- Inquire by phone if there is any problem with your services. Reiterate your commitment to the project, and express your expectation of getting paid on time.

- If this is not successful, call for a face-to-face meeting. Bring along a senior principal to emphasize the importance of the issue. Get commitment as to a specific date, and offer to send a courier to pick up the check.

- Keep a positive demeanor throughout this process without losing firmness with the client. State that you have subconsultants to pay and cannot jeopardize either the project or your relationship with these subconsultants by not paying them on time.

- Write a letter expressing your serious concern, reiterate all of the above items, state there was no indication whatsoever that the services were not within expectations, and suggest that "perhaps we are going ahead too fast" or "should temporarily stop if funds are a problem." Depending on circumstances, a letter may be sent by Registered Mail, which can be a very effective attention-getting device.

If the client does not provide payment or an explanation and a commitment or plan to pay that is satisfactory, the situation must be discussed with the appropriate project manager or principal-in-charge and all work stopped until the payment situation is resolved.

The next steps are more drastic. Start by hinting at collection action, then "other avenues." Having a lawyer draft a statement of claim (Without Prejudice) is one possibility to be weighed carefully in terms of its cost-benefit ratio.

If these problems continue, at some point the decision has to be made to send strong signals to the client, including:

- Slowing down work considerably.

- Not responding to queries, requests for information, prints, etc.

- Asking that only the principal-in-charge and/or the project manager take the client's calls.

Never offer rebates, discounts, or changes in payment terms. This will only encourage the client to delay payment in the future.

Document everything in writing. Keep track of times when copies of invoices, statements, etc., were repeatedly sent to the client. Keep transmittals and copies of such documents handy in a separate folder, to be filed away only when the matter is resolved

Giving Money Back to the Client

Most professional services contracts are based on some type of cost-plus-fee arrangement with a budgetary not-to-exceed amount. Such contracts have traditionally been managed like the old television game of "The Price is Right." The design firm tries to spend up to the not-to-exceed amount without going over. This approach has been so commonplace that clients expect to spend the full not-to-exceed amount on every project. In evaluating competitive proposals, clients often use proposed not-to-exceed budgets as a way of judging which design firm will provide its services at the lowest cost.

Design firms can dramatically improve client relations by planning to spend less than the not-to-exceed amounts of their contracts. By returning 2-5% of the authorized expenditure value to the client, the firm presents an image of being efficient and concerned about the client's money The fact that very few design firms employ this practice will make it even more impressive to the client. Doing it on a regular basis will also reduce the client's tendency to compare the firm's not-to-exceed estimates with those of competing firms.

How do you handle projects whose scope and level of effort during the course of the job? Most design firms try to handle these extra efforts with the original authorization if at all possible. Their intent is to give the client a "little extra" in the name of good client relations. Unfortunately the design firm usually discovers in time that this extra service cannot be accommodated within the original authorization, then has to ask for an increase as the project is nearing completion and running out of money.

A much better approach is for the design firm to request an increase in authorization as soon as the scope change or extra level of effort is identified. The client does not necessarily have to formally amend the contract, but should agree that such an amendment will be made if required prior to reaching the existing authorization. At the end of the project, the design firm can total all the extra work activities and show the client that the actual costs are less than authorized amount.

Follow Through on Client Feedback

Many firms have a process for offering evaluations to clients and the closing of a project. But what do you do with these evaluation forms after you have gone to the trouble of getting them? Here are a few ideas to consider:

- Don't file them away in some folder that never again sees the light of day—make use of them!

- Review the evaluations with your entire project team together. Make sure each member of the team understands both the positive and the negative feedback.

- Create action items that address the areas needing improvement. Assign responsibility to the project team member(s) who can (and will) make a difference.

- Share the evaluations with other project teams so you can learn from one another. There should be no secrets when it comes to making improvements. Candor and honesty among project teams is the most effective way to create added value in the processes, products, and services offered by your firm.

- Screen out any comments concerning specific individuals, and deal with them in private. Incorporate both good and bad comments into your personal evaluation program. Make sure your team is aware that their performance, as judged by clients, is very important and will impact their advancement and compensation within the firm.

Stay in Contact with Clients to Keep Their Work Coming

Here are twelve ways you can stay in touch with your client after the project is complete. This increases the chances that you are in line for future work.

1. Arrange a walkthrough of the current project.

2. Ask the client for three possible leads for new clients or projects.

3. Inquire about the condition of the job six months after completion.

4. Ask the client if they have any additional projects.

5. Request a debriefing on the project.

6. Ask for a letter of recommendation.

7. Interview the client on a technical issue for a newsletter or article for general publication.

8. Ask the client to review your marketing plan.

9. Arrange for the client to speak at a professional function.

10. Request a mid-project debriefing outside of a regular project meeting.

11. Arrange a tour of decorated homes at holiday time.

12. Send your client a birthday or anniversary card.

Statistics show you must "touch" a potential client at least seven times before you win a new project — it takes that much time to build rapport. Focusing your "touches" on present or past clients bears much more fruit because you already have an established relationship. So use it to your advantage!

Five Ways to Save a Dissatisfied Client

Turning unhappy clients into loyal ones is part of every firm's client retention program. A lost client will cost your firm much more than one job. The marketing costs associated with having to replace that client are often much more than the costs of "saving" an established client.

Focusing on client satisfaction and viewing all issues from the client's perspective should be your firm's initial priorities.

In addition, your firm's client retention program should include a written plan of action for client recovery if a problem arises.

Your plan needs to include the following points:

1. **Determine the costs of mending client dissatisfaction.** For example, consider revising part of the design at no cost. The cost for this revision may save the client for your firm.

2. **Establish a training program for technical staff**, focusing on client recovery tactics.

3. **Get your client to talk**, allowing you to act on the complaints. Take your client to lunch in the middle of the job. Ask him or her how the job is proceeding and what could be improved.

4. **Anticipate problems.** Every member of your staff who is involved with the client should be on the alert for any problem that could arise—and have a course of action to correct it.

5. **Respond quickly.** Most clients will respond favorably if you solve their problem straight away.

CHAPTER 8

MANAGING QUALITY AND RISKS

A Sample Quality Assurance Policy for Small Firms

The following is an example of a simple quality assurance program used by real firms. It is made up of four areas: planning, studies, design projects, large projects, and client satisfaction.

Planning Studies

1. All reports will be peer reviewed prior to sending to the client. Where the schedule allows, this review will be conducted prior to sending the draft report to the client.

2. All department secretaries will be instructed not to mail final reports unless they are signed by both the project manager and the peer reviewer. Exceptions will require prior approval by the Principal-in-Charge.

Design Projects

1. All design projects will have an assigned technical director who is responsible for assuring that an adequate independent review is conducted before the plans and specifications are issued for bids. The technical director will be nominated by the project manager and approved by the Principal-in-Charge. (The Principal-in-Charge may serve as technical director).

2. Plans and specifications will be signed off by (1) the registered architect/engineer in responsible charge of the work and (2) the technical director prior to issuing for bids.

3. All department secretaries will should not mail final plans and specifications unless they are signed by both the project manager and technical director. Any exceptions require prior approval by the Principal-in-Charge.

Large Projects

1. Projects with an initial fee over $100,000 require a written Quality Control Plan that specifies what types of reviews will be made, who will conduct the reviews and when the reviews will be scheduled.

2. Project managers for large projects will present a status report to the Principal-in-Charge and the President on the first Wednesday of each month. The status report will include financial status,

client relations and status of implementing the reviews in the Quality Control Plan.

Client Satisfaction

1. A Principal-in-Charge will be assigned to each major client. His or her responsibility is to assure the work meets the client's satisfaction. The client will be advised of this arrangement and encouraged to come to the Principal-in-Charge for any issues that are not being handled adequately by the Project Manager. The Principal-in-Charge will also contact the client from time to time to verify satisfaction with the work.

2. Every January and June, the Marketing Director will send a one-page evaluation form to each major client requesting written feedback from the client regarding all the firm's work for that client during the past six months. Letters will be prepared for the signature of the Principal-in-Charge for that client. Where work is being performed for multiple client representatives, each representative will be sent a copy of the evaluation form.

3. Two weeks after sending the evaluation form, the Principal-in-Charge will follow up. If the form has not been returned, the client will be asked to please fill it out. If it have been returned by then, the client will be asked to amplify the process.

Six Tactics for Managing Project Risk

Make sure these six steps are in place on each and every project your firm delivers. Share and discuss these steps with your project managers today.

1. **Understand the job.** What, when, who, how, for how much. If you don't have or can't be sure you can get the answers for each of these, you're not ready to propose—let alone undertake—the project.

2. **Understand the risks.** There is risk to everything; the key is knowing where it may pop up, and how to manage it.

   Risks come from different parts of a project:

   - The risk that the job isn't real, or wired to someone else and you'll spend time and money chasing an illusion.

   - The risk in the particular client. What it the client's need, approach, intent, objective, reputation, intelligence? How well do you fit with that profile?

   - The risks that come from the client's RFP development staff. Do they understand what they need? How have they allocated the project risks?

   - The risks from the project description (scope of services). Is the description clear and well thought out? Is it tight enough to tell you what to do, but not so tight that you have no room to bring value to the project?

- The risk from the client's project manager. Have you worked with him? Is he a budget person, a technical person, or an administrator? What does this mean in terms of project success?

3. **Look at the details for risks and opportunities.** The details are in the contract document. Read them yourself—every time—before you commit the firm to doing the project.

4. **Get your project managers to tame project risk.** For every identified risk there must be an effective strategy. These strategies include:

   - Change risks by redefinition or clarification.

   - Valuing the risk: "I need to get this for that."

   - Saying "No" at least once on the way to "Yes."

   - Pan and budget extra resources to balance the risk allocation.

   - Identify who is best able to manage risk.

   - Transfer specific risks to insurance, or subcontractors through contract provisions.

   - Document how the strategy is implemented. Don't keep reinventing the risk management wheel.

5. **Quantify, value, and evaluate.** The project proposal should contain a list of quantities for each service. Vagueness will always get interpreted against you. Include options, substitutions, unit values for additional units, a fixed price option for a list of extras, etc.

6. **Check your bags!** Did you get what you bargained for? The contract is what counts, not the telephone conversation, not the notes of the meeting. If it is not in the contract directly or by reference, you didn't get it.

Managing Risk: It Takes More than Insurance

The challenge for design-builders is managing risk without requiring excessive contingency.

For the contractor, the risk of professional liability as it relates to design adequacy is new. For the design firm, new risks arise on the construction side, such as:

Construction scheduling (and related liquidated damages)

Management of construction forces

Jobsite safety

Procurement of equipment

Providing general warranty

Guarantee of construction work

There are several ways to manage this additional risk. A number of insurance underwriters are now offering add-on riders to protect contractors for professional liability risk. Like- wise, a number of professional liability underwriters offer coverage for design professionals for construction activities.

The key is ensuring that insurance vehicles are utilized as part of a comprehensive risk management program and are not the only risk management tool. To this end, gaps in coverage or overlapping coverages need to be coordinated with all contracting parties in concert with their insurance providers.

An additional strategy is for members of the design-build team to retain specific risk for their portion of the project scope, such as the design or the construction. With this approach, sharing of profits must be proportional to the risks retained by each party.

Assess the Quality of Your Projects

There are certain criteria against which to evaluate your projects. Following are the most important ones:

- How well has the project scope been defined and communicated at every level on the job? Is the work being accomplished in accordance with the requirements?

- Is full and effective use being made of standard company guidelines and procedures?

- Does everyone understand the attitude required for a successful client relationship? If not, what is being done to improve this lack of understanding?

- Are any quality parameters being measured? What are the results of these measurements?

- How is the corrective action process being implemented on the project to resolve known problems?

- Project meetings must be conducted in a positive, team-building way. Discussions about existing problems should focus on ways to improve methods of producing work that conforms to the requirements.

Project managers should:

- Encourage suggestions on how to prevent problems.

- Promote the performance of error-free work.

- Train each member to recognize his/her role in achieving the project goal.

Your Role in Quality Control

One of the most common mistakes made in quality control is for a reviewer to be given a set of documents and told, "Here, review these and mark any errors you find." Such vague instructions fail to provide explicit guidance as to what kind of review is expected. The following is a description of several different kinds of reviews typically conducted on design projects. It's your job to assess which of these elements are required for a given design, and at what stages of completion the documents should be reviewed.

- **Conceptual Review.** One or more independent reviewers should check the basic concepts to make sure that the facility will function properly, given the project's budget and schedule constraints.

- **Intradisciplinary Review.** This ensures that an independent, experienced person from each discipline checks the applicable calculations, drawings, and specifications produced by that discipline. Although the review cannot be done by the person who performed the design, it can be done by another project team member. For example, if two experienced structural engineers are working on different portions of a design, one can easily check the work done by the other because they are already familiar with the project.

- **Interdiscipline Review.** Even if the work of each discipline is flawless, problems may arise due to inconsistencies between the disciplines. To find these problems, one or more individuals should perform a detailed interdisciplinary review to assure consistency between disciplines.

- **Drawing-Specification Cross-Check.** This hould be done by an individual who reviews the specifications page by page, identifying information that might also appear elsewhere on drawings and specifications.

- **Multifacility Cross-Check.** For large projects that involve multiple buildings or facilities, there needs to be a review for inconsistencies between these buildings.

- **Vendor Review.** Vendor reviews can identify equipment incompatibilities, out-of-date specifications, and inappropriate materials. They can also provide other requested information such as costs and delivery times.

- **Constructability Review.** Even if the drawings and specifications are technically correct and consistent, the design may be difficult or impossible for a contractor to construct. This problem can often turn into costly change orders. The best person to perform this review is a construction contractor or former contractor.

- **Operability Review.** Unlike problems that occur during design and construction, operations and maintenance problems often plague the project for many years after the design firm has completed its work—with potentially devastating effects on your firm's reputation. This review should be done by the owner's building manager, or the person responsible for operating the completed building. If the owner's maintenance manager is not available, someone should be retained who has operated a similar facility.

Three Major Factors for Successful Quality Control

1. **Incorporate QA/QC into your budget.** Include QA/QC as a line item in your budget, and sell your client on its importance—both in the proposal and in early meetings. Following your firm's QA/QC plan is not an option; it's a requirement, regardless of whether or not your client pays for it.

2. **Make realistic staff assignments.** Many employees lack the experience and judgment to handle a project's technical aspects. So be sure to assign each task to the most qualified person.

    Be aware of your team's strengths and limitations—compensating, when needed, with more intense supervision. Assignments may need to be daily or twice-weekly, instead of weekly or biweekly.

3. **Beware of project complexity.** Long-lasting or complex projects require painstaking coordination and invite error. Employee turnover on a big or multi-disciplined project can impede communication, and a small, undetected mistake passed on to other teams can magnify the consequences over time.

    Make each discipline responsible for QC in its individual sub-area. Assign a task leader with the knowledge, support, and communication skills to ensure his or her team follows through with required QC procedures. When disciplines share information, make sure each task leader knows the level of detail involved and the impact of the correct information on the other disciplines' tasks.

How Do Your Clients Define Quality?

From a client's viewpoint, defining design quality is not nearly as clear-cut as it is for lawyers defining standards of quality. Many perceptions and expectations other than the actual design quality enter into a client's evaluation of your work.

For example, look at the complaints one public works client had and the way the design firm assuaged the client's concerns by implementing appropriate criteria:

Client Complaints

- **Submittal of obviously unchecked documents**
  Require documentation of completed QC check of calculations, drawings, and specs prior to each submittal

- **Finishing the design by addendum**
  Have no addenda regarding design deficiencies

- **Excessive spreads among bidders**
  Restrict spread among lowest 3 bidders to less than 10 percent

- **Complaints about the design from the selected subcontractor**
  Allow evaluation from selected subcontractor

- **Too many utility conflicts**
  Ensure no unexpected conflicts with documented utilities

- **Change orders resulting from design deficiencies**
  Allow less than 2 percent of construction cost for change orders due to design deficiencies

Make sure you understand your clients' hot buttons for quality.

QC That Really Works

Every A/E/C firm professes to follow strict quality control procedures, but far too often the process breaks down in actual practice. One design firm we know has a quality control program that truly works. Here's how:

The project manager prepares a detailed work plan before work commences.

The key elements of the work plan include:

- The person responsible for each task
- The time schedule
- The fee budget available
- The scheduled quality control reviews (as noted below)

The firm's experts on this project type meet with the project team at the beginning of the concept development stage to decide what alternatives will and will not work. This eliminates a lot of blind alleys.

These experts are brought back for another review before the conceptual design is finalized. Once approved at this state, the design concept is not changed unless an error is changed.

A special quality control team reviews the first check set to make sure the project will work mechanically, structurally, etc. At this early stage of the final design, it's not too late to make changes.

This same team does the final review at the 90 percent stage and cleans up the loose ends.

This type of quality control program is followed on every project, regardless. As a result, the firm's loss experience is negligible.

Value Engineering: Not Always a Great Value

Formal value engineering (VE) is the systematic up-front review of a project design to obtain optimum value for a construction project. Its goal is to eliminate or redesign features that add cost but that add nothing to the building's quality, life, utility or appearance. This according to the Professional Liability Agents Network (PLAN), a select group of insurance agencies specializing in risk management and loss prevention programs for architects, engineers, environmental consultants, accounts, and lawyers.

Certified value engineers analyze design concepts, specifications, construction techniques, materials, building systems, building types, and up-front versus life-cycle cost to arrive at the best overall value for the structure.

Scheduled VE

The certified approach to value engineering is planned at the outset of the project as an integral part of the design process. Through brainstorming sessions, the entire VE team—owner rep, designer, contractor, construction manager, and consultants—identifies potential savings, large or small. The owner and the prime design professional evaluate these findings and discuss the likely impact of the group's recommendations on the quality and the initial and life cycle costs of the project.

Key to the cost-effectiveness of this approach is the understanding that the owner's decisions are to be implemented by the prime design professional during the design development phase, without the need to go back and revise schematic design documents.

Unscheduled ("informal") VE

This very different process is usually marketed to project owners as a cost-cutting tool, and typically performed by design professionals, general contractors, construction managers, or cost estimators who have no VE certification.

Rather than offering a formal, prescheduled value engineering process, the "informal" VE consultant provides advice after completion of the schematic design and design development phase. With this advice, and with consultation with the prime design professional and the cost consultant, the owner renders cost-critical decisions for the next stage of design.

At the worst, this informal process can deteriorate into second-guessing of the original designer by the contractor, construction manager, or other consultants hired to cut up-front cost with little concern for long-term value. This kind of value engineering can undermine the designer of record and reduce the quality and safety of the project.

Unscheduled VE can also exclude or severely limit the involvement of key team members. Typically, the VE firm unilaterally makes "cost-cutting" recommendations to the owner. The owner then decides what changes to make in the project scope and the building system or materials, and directs the design professional to revise the design concepts and documents accordingly.

Such an adversarial process allows for a greater likelihood of conflict and claims. It also creates greater potential for error in revising the construction documents after bids have been received: the tight time demands for changes may prevent proper coordination and checking. Finally there is often pressure to accept lesser quality or inferior products or building systems—although these cheaper alternatives may markedly increase the costs of operation and maintenance over the life of the project.

A reminder: The above material is for informational purposes only. Before taking action that could have legal or other important consequences, PSMJ Resources suggests you speak with a qualified legal professional who can guide you through your own unique circumstances.

Protecting Yourself from VE Drawbacks

Clearly, for the designer of record, value engineering raises many questions and concerns, according to the

Professional Liability Agents Network (PLAN), a select group of insurance agencies specializing in risk management and loss prevention programs for architects, engineers, environmental consultants, accountants, and lawyers.

Some of these concerns:

- If your design is evaluated, what is the extent of your responsibility to modify it?

- Are you expected to perform substantial redesign work with no additional compensation?

- Do you have the right to disagree with the value engineer's recommendations? ...believe are appropriate?

- What happens if the changes affect the permits or licenses obtained for the original design?

- What if a lawsuit results from the redesign changes—are you liable?

According to PLAN, in any project where value engineering is contemplated, certified specialists should direct VE. Furthermore, compensation for value engineers should never be based on savings carved out of the original design. Such an arrangement creates a clear conflict of interest.

Contractual Protection

If you are the design professional of record and you know or believe value engineering will be performed on your project, anticipate it in your contract, PLAN says.

Develop a clear understanding with your client as to the extent of your obligations to redesign in order to accommodate any decisions based on the value engineering.

Your contract should include a clause to limit responsibility for redesign and to give you the ability to object to the recommendations of the value engineer. In addition, make certain any redesign you provide will be performed as an additional service and compensated accordingly.

If you feel that implementing certain recommendations could threaten public health and safety, document your concerns thoroughly and follow up with both the VE and your client to reach a resolution.

Also, you may have a duty to notify appropriate building safety agencies in accordance with your obligations under your license.

Beware of Unscheduled Value Engineering

Formal value engineering (VE) is the systematic up-front review of a project design to obtain optimum value for a construction project, used to eliminate features that add cost but that add nothing to the building's quality, life, utility, or appearance. This approach is planned at the outset of the project as an integral part of the design process.

Yet sometimes owners bring in an unscheduled, "informal" consultant to provide advice after the completion of the schematic design and development phase. This has the potential for numerous problems:

- Introducing value engineering late in the project—particularly during or after the construction documents phase—is risky and expensive. You and your project team will face a whole new set of problems and liabilities.

- Late VE can disrupt the design and construction drawing preparation process. It may mean rethinking fundamental decisions as well as subsequent redesign and reproduction of construction documents to reflect the changes. All this will require added time that impacts your schedule and budget.

Bringing in new players late in the design process usually introduces new agendas, sometimes undisclosed, and perhaps differing sets of values. The result can mean reduced quality, increased life-cycle cost, or threatened project safety—all resulting in increased liabilities.

Use Benchmarking to Improve Quality

A relatively quick and inexpensive way to solve quality problems is to identify someone who has already solved the same problem and copy the solution. This technique, known as "benchmarking" can be used within the same firm, within the same industry, or outside the industry.

Let's look at how an engineering company recently used benchmarking to solve a common quality problem—slow collection of accounts receivable.

Internal Studies

The first step was internal benchmarking, that is, looking at various offices within the firm to determine which offices consistently had the fastest cash collections. The following differences were noted in the procedures used at the most successful offices:

- Individuals who prepared the invoices were degreed accountants with over five years of experience. Less successful offices often used inexperienced clerks to perform the task.

- Invoicing and collections were the primary responsibility of a single individual. In less successful offices, this responsibility was often disbursed among several people.

- Project managers were given three working days to review invoices; if no comments were received in that time, invoices were mailed to the clients. In less successful offices, PMs were allowed to delay mailing of invoices for weeks until they were able to review them.

Other A/E Firms

The next step in the benchmarking process was to identify other design firms that had excellent records of collecting accounts quickly. These additional techniques were identified:

- Large projects were billed weekly or biweekly rather than monthly.

- Labor costs were billed separately form expenses so that questions about minor expenses didn't delay payment.

- Sample invoices were attached to the contract and reviewed with the client prior to mailing the first invoice.

Other Industries

Finally, successful firms in other industries were studied to see if some of their techniques might be applicable in speeding payment of accounts. These procedures were identified:

- A late charge of 1.5 percent was automatically billed for all accounts more than 45 days past due (from a dentist).

- Original invoices were sent directly to clients' accounts payable departments in addition to being sent to the clients' project managers (from an accounting firm).

- Up-front retainers were requested in the amount of approximately two months' charges. These retainers were then held until the end of the project (from a law firm).

With these ideas consolidated into one strategy, the total capital turnaround was reduced from an average of over 100 days to 70 days!

✍ Project Specification Checklist

❑ Have available standard specifications been used in the preparation of the draft?

❑ Are the specifications complete and clear enough to properly specify design, construction, and conformance requirements?

❑ Are the proper codes, standards and processes referenced?

❑ Are required tests and inspections specified?

❑ Is the proper test and inspection documentation specified?

❑ Are construction and test requirements feasible?

❑ Are the acceptance criteria specified and are they realistic?

❑ Are provisions made for special construction procedures necessary to keep the facility in operation at all times during construction?

❑ Are calibration requirements for measuring and testing equipment spelled out and cleaning, storage, and handling requirements specified?

❑ Are construction tolerances executable from a practical and design point of view?

✍ Project Specification Checklist (Cont.)

❑ Are the specifications project-specific, with the correct project title and client name?

❑ Do the specifications prescribe and allow for a clear phasing of construction?

❑ Are all equipment items cross-checked with the drawings?

❑ Do all cross-referenced specification items exist?

Managing Site Safety Risks

Design professionals encounter site safety risks at all stages of the design and construction process. At each stage, you should implement safeguards to minimize and manage those risks. Practice the following recommendations:

- Know the law concerning site safety in the jurisdiction where the project will be constructed. Typically, most state statutes impose principal responsibility for site safety on the contractor, but in some jurisdictions, burdens are placed on owners, who may shift that burden to the design professional.

- Understand the special risks imposed by various areas of design work and how these risks can be allocated among all of the project participants. By

way of examples, there are unique risks in
underground construction, design of erection
sequences and temporary support for steel frame
construction and a host of other areas.

- At the time of contract negotiation, give careful
  consideration to the scope of construction site
  services—are these services to be intermittent or
  continuous? Is one site representative sufficient
  for the scale of the project? What is the owner's
  expectation regarding the degree to which the
  engineer will be onsite and to what degree can the
  engineer observe the contractor's work?

- Owners will seek to keep costs down, but the
  engineer should ensure that the contract reflects
  the quantity and quality of construction
  observation services the owner is willing to pay
  for.

- Avoid identifying construction site services as
  "inspection" or "monitoring," and especially
  "supervision." You should be "observing" the
  contractor's work for conformance with the intent
  on design.

- Ensure that your contract with the owner is in
  harmony with the owner/contractor contract as
  regards duties for control of the site and
  responsibility for the contractor's means and
  methods, as well as responsibility for site safety.

Train field staff for the services they are to provide:

- Never communicate, either orally or in writing, direction to the contractor, approval of means and methods, or comments on the procedures employed, except as necessary to report observations to the owner.

- Know who to contact and what to do in the event an unsafe situation is encountered, including when to leave the site if corrective steps are not promptly taken by the contractor.

- Ensure that site activities stay within the scope of the specific duties to observe as set out in the contract documents.

- Document unsafe conditions and promptly report to the design firm's supervisors for further direction.

CHAPTER 9

CONTROLLING THE PROJECT

PM Checklist for Project Success

Tight budgets, schedules, and other constraints impede success in a market where there are fewer and fewer opportunities to recover from mistakes—that's the chaotic environment in which we work. You need all of the help you can get, and help in business management comes with practice and structure.

The following is a checklist of the elements that contribute to project success:

- Know what you are doing before you start.
- Carefully choose the team.
- Participate in proposal writing.
- Obtain full authority to manage and control the work.
- Develop your people skills.
- Set sensible, achievable goals.

- Document each significant project event clearly and promptly.

- Produce project documentation efficiently.

- Use a simple scheduling method.

- Remember that speed is critical, but double-edged. Instill a sense of urgency in your staff, but stress quality.

- Don't just track overspending, cut the budget! Look for ways to save money.

How to Schedule Project Meetings

Design professionals waste valuable time because of poorly scheduled meetings.

DON'T:

- Schedule meetings every day of the week.

- Schedule meetings so one meeting runs into another.

- Schedule meetings away from the office, which require travel time.

- Plan meetings without an agenda.

- Schedule meetings without confirming who will attend.

- Arrange lunch meetings (eat between meetings).

DO:

- Plan project meetings for Tuesdays and Thursdays.

- Schedule all "away- from-the-office" meetings on Tuesday.

- Schedule all "in-the- office" meetings on Thursday.

- Try to limit each meeting to less than one hour.

- Have an agenda for every meeting that specifies the end time.

- Schedule an hour between meetings.

- Telephone everyone on the day before the meeting for a final commitment.

- Sit in your place 15 minutes before the meeting is scheduled to start.

- Stress that meetings should happen in your office rather than away.

By following these simple rules, you will make your entire week more efficient, saving time and money for the firm.

21 BEST Project Management Tactics

Best time to call a contractor	7 a.m.
Best time to call a client	Tuesday: 8:45 a.m.
Best time to run a meeting	11 a.m.
Best day to hold meetings	Tuesday
Best time to plan manpower	Monday, 8 a.m.
Best day to mail invoices	23rd of the month (to get paid by the 1st)
Best time to open	4:30 p.m.
Best time to eat with clients	At breakfast
Best meeting format	Stand-up meetings
Best way to control meetings	Take meeting minutes yourself
Best position among six firms competing in a presentation	Last
Best form of contract	Lump-sum, with a well-defined scope
Best employee	One who initiates action
Best length of workday	Nine hours maximum
Best day to avoid interruptions	Saturday

Best time to get things done	Before office hours
Best way to avoid conflict	Use straight communication
Best title on a business card	None at all
Best interoffice memo	Handwritten
Best time to fire someone	Monday, 9 a.m.
Best project manager	One who instructs team daily

Six Essential Project Control Tools

The application of basic project control tools enhance the project team's abilities to keep the team informed and focus on the demobilization and project close-out objective. They include:

- **Project completion schedule**–to provide a daily focus on the project demobilization and close-out activities. The schedule is used as the communication tool in the project status meeting and to assist in establishing the Plan of the Day activities that will focus the work planned on the critical tasks for project demobilization and close-out.

- **Action items list**–used to assign responsibility and track key actions required to facilitate the demobilization and close-out. Typical information included in an Action Items List are: Action Required, Requester, Responsible Individual and

Group, the Required Date and Forecast/Actual completion date.

- **Subcontractor punch list**–similar to the Action Items List, this punch list is intended to track incomplete or open items for the subcontract when the work is essentially completed.

- **Vendor notification list**–develop a list of leased or rental agreements sorted in reverse order by the days prior to the project demobilization date for discontinuation of services or for equipment pick-up. A typical notification list would be organized by the actions required 30, 14 or 7 days prior to demobilization. On a recent project, the vendor required a 30-day written notice prior to the pick-up of the rented Fax machine, resulting in an extra monthly rental charge due to the lack of timely notification.

- **Project team de-staffing plan**–As project tasks or phases are completed, personnel should be taken off the project as soon as practical. The De-staffing plan should reflect remaining job-hours and forecast release dates for each individual team member. This plan should be made available to the team members and the appropriate managers responsible for reassignment of the project team.

- **Cost control**–Although this paper focused on planning and execution of demobilization and project close-out, the project must remain focused on cost control and cost awareness during this final phase of the project. Cost and schedule work together and a shorter schedule will usually equate to lower costs and vice versa. Budget limitations will also focus the project team's attention on the early completion of demobilization and close-out actions.

Keep an Eye on Your Backlog

The ups and downs of the design industry means you rarely have the same staff requirements over time. However, staff-level planning can offer some stability. Such planning answers four questions:

1. Is there a staff shortage or surplus?
2. Is it temporary or long-term?
3. What kinds of people do we need?
4. How can we alleviate the shortage or surplus?

Either you alone or a group of PMs can coordinate the planning. Regardless, the key input comes from the PMs who report on their projects' progress and requirements.

The simplest way to figure staffing requirements is to monitor the project backlog. Here are two steps to take:

1. Each week, determine the number of hours remaining on active projects in your office.
2. Divide this number by the total hours available from qualified staff members. The quotient will equal the weeks of backlog for your office.

When you calculate the backlog, count only internal staff; exclude the contributions of outside consultants. Also, always use the estimated hours needed to complete the job.

Monitor your backlog trend constantly. If it shrinks over several months, put an extra focus on marketing. If it grows, look for additional staff or other creative ways of handling the increased workload.

How to Avoid Jobsite Safety Liability

Because jobsite safety is such a serious liability concern, you should become knowledgeable of the risks and remedies. Design firms must avoid any contract language that could make them liable for safety and instruct their staff to conduct themselves cautiously while on the jobsite.

Under no circumstances should you accept a contract clause that makes you responsible for any losses or injuries that occur at the jobsite. Also, avoid any language in a client-drafted agreement that calls for your "supervision" on a jobsite, as well as any language that calls for you to "assure strict compliance" with plans, specifications or any health or safety plans or programs. Your responsibilities for construction observation at the jobsite should be limited specifically to determining general conformance with the design.

Scope of Services

When developing your scope of services, carefully define your construction-phase services to avoid assuming responsibility for jobsite safety. This is especially important if you are offering full-time, resident or expanded field services.

Make it clear to the client and the contractor that you are not responsible in any way for the means, methods, sequence, procedures, techniques or scheduling of construction activities—or for jobsite safety. These duties rightfully belong with the general contractor, who has the largest degree of control of the jobsite.

Shop Drawings

One level of protection is to establish and follow appropriate procedures with respect to shop drawing review. Your principal concern is to avoid reviewing and commenting on any aspect of shop drawings that relates to jobsite safety. To handle shop drawing reviews effectively:

- Clearly describe in your client contract your duties in reviewing submittals. State that you will not review shop drawings for anything related to the means, methods, techniques, sequences and procedures of construction, or to safety procedures and programs. Spell out, too, the individual items that are the contractor's duty, such as dimensions, gauges, quantities and weights.

- Define exactly what types of shop drawings you will review and inform the contractor of your decision via contract documents. Also, advise contractors that you will not review shop drawings not specifically requested or approved.

- Require that the contractor provide and adhere to a schedule of submittals. Allow adequate time for thorough shop drawing review and obtain an appropriate fee.

- Be careful how you indicate shop drawing "approval." Use a shop drawing stamp to indicate you have reviewed submittals for "general conformance with the design concept," or similar language.

- Do not allow contractors to use a shop drawing to obtain approval for a variation. Require contractors to review and approve in writing all shop drawings before submitting them to you.

The above material is for informational purposes only. Before taking action that could have legal or other important consequences, PSMJ Resources suggests you speak with a qualified legal professional who can guide you through your own unique circumstances.

Avoid These Project Paths to Failure

Here are some common but sometimes hidden warning signs that you are headed down a path towards project failure.

- Accounts Receivable/payment times start to slip more than the usual durations previously experienced on project to date.

- The client is surprised at your team's understanding of project scope.

- The client is surprised at your team's understanding of his or her own responsibilities.

- A new client project manager is brought in to complete the project.

- A new major client or subconsultant team members suddenly emerge.

- Work is submitted to you by subconsultants (or from you to the client) incomplete with addenda or multiple revisions required to fully complete.

- The contract has not been signed even though more you than 10% into the project work hours expended.

- The percent of money spent on projects is higher than percent complete.

- No project management plan has been completed for the project and/or client.

- You are not using an action item list to track actions or assignments for the project team.

- You are surprised by the number of hours team members are charging to the project.

- You do not consistently attend regular in-house project status reviews and/or fail to issue timely status reports and meeting minutes.

- Change orders have been submitted but the client has not formally approved them.

- Work on added scope is going ahead though no written authorization has been received from client.

- The project includes a new design or construction technology or CAD/BIM requirements that the team is unfamiliar with.

- Client CAD or building detail standards have not been discussed.

- Requests for client information, reviews, existing conditions information, etc. go unmet and schedule is not adjusted accordingly and no documentation is issued.

Many of these unwanted surprises are issues that you can prevent with the proper management approach. Keep this list handy and look out for any red flags that could lead to bigger problems later on in the project.

Beyond the Plan—Managing Conflict

Good project managers realize that conflicts are inevitable and that procedures and techniques have to be developed to resolve them. If you're not careful, you could easily worsen a conflict by not knowing how to manage it.

Once a conflict occurs, be careful to take these vital first steps:

- Study the problem and collect all available information.

- Approach the situation methodically.

- Set the appropriate atmosphere.

In setting the appropriate atmosphere, you must make it clear that you are willing to participate with others involved. In addition, you must clearly state the upcoming meeting's objectives, establish the meeting's credibility and sanction conflict-resolving efforts.

During the meeting between conflicting parties, you, as PM, should be aware of the logical steps and the sequence of events that should be taken. You should:

1. **Set the climate: establish a willingness to participate.**

2. **Analyze the images.** How do you see yourself and others, how do they see you?

3. **Collect the information and get feelings out in the open.**

4. **Define the problem.** Define/clarify all positions.

5. **Share the information.** Make sure the information is available to all concerned.

6. **Set the appropriate priorities.** Develop working sessions for setting priorities and timetables.

7. **Organize the group.** Form cross-functional problem-solving groups.

8. **Problem solve**. Obtain cross-functional involvement, secure commitments and set priorities and
   the timetable.

9. **Develop the action plan**. Get commitment.

10. **Implement the work**. Take action on the plan.

11. **Follow up**. Obtain feedback on the implement-
    tation of the **action** plan.

Once the conflict has been defined and a meeting is
deemed necessary, the PM should understand the conflict
minimization procedures. You should:

- Pause and think before reacting.

- Build trust.

- Try to understand the conflict motives.

- Keep the meeting under control.

- Listen to all parties in an unbiased manner.

- Maintain a give-and-take attitude.

- Tactfully edify others on your views.

- Be willing to be edified by others on their views.

- Be willing to admit when you are wrong.

Documenting the Project

Maintain complete documentation on every job. The
following general administration information should be
kept in your project files:

- Records of all communications with the prospective client before the contract is signed.

- Names, addresses, telephone numbers of the client and client's representative(s), including billing information.

- Contracts and agreements.

- Documents related to fee negotiations and agreements, including scope of services.

- Documents related to design and construction schedules, including the client's preliminary schedule, approved schedules, and any changes.

- Documents related to construction budgets, including the client's preliminary budget, approved budget and any changes during the course of the project.

- Records of communications with the client after the contract is signed.

- Records of communications with other parties involved with the project.

- Fee and staffing allocations.

- Invoices, statements and backup documents related to client billing.

- Accounts receivable records.

- Records of expenses billed or assigned to the project including expense invoices and consultant's billing.

- Any other accounting records pertaining to the project.

📋 Project Report Checklist

Use the following checklist as a guide for establishing and checking the overall appearance of project reports:

❏ Is the report written in the preferred second or third person (we conclude, it is concluded...) rather than first person?

❏ Is the language clear, concise, and unambiguous?

❏ Is the meaning and intent of each statement clear?

❏ Does the writing style help to keep the reader's attention, or does it inhibit reading and understanding?

❏ Are sentences made excessively long with the use of conjunctions (such as "and," "or," "etc.")?

❏ Do paragraphs define discrete ideas, and are they limited to only a few sentences?

❏ Is vocabulary simple to the extent possible?

❏ Are graphics consistent in format throughout the report?

❏ Are exhibits legible after size reduction?

❏ Are exhibits and tables properly labeled and numbered?

❏ Are proper scales shown on drawings and exhibits, and are the scales still accurate after size reduction?

🛍 Project Report Checklist (Cont.)

❏ Are exhibits and tables properly referenced in the text?

❏ Is spelling correct on all exhibits and illustrations?

❏ Are two engineers' seals required (author and principal)?

❏ Is page numbering correct and consistent with the table of contents and index?

❏ Are headers and/or footers needed, and, if so, are they consistent?

Project Manager's Greatest Challenges

As part of the PSMJ Project Manager's Bootcamp course evaluations, we ask our attendees what is the biggest problem that their firms face today.

Here's a sampling of project management challenges and frustrations:

- Can't find enough qualified employees
- Mounting employee frustration with assignments and over- loading
- Cost overruns due to reworking on projects
- Meeting budgets
- Team members who fail to meet obligations

- Balancing workloads with staffing
- Changes in technology vs. reduction in client base
- Being proactive rather than reactive to RFPs
- Team planning and time management
- Maintaining workload for staff
- Keeping profitability high
- Marketing and keeping/ recruiting good staff
- Attracting new clients
- Becoming more efficient on projects
- Juggling multiple projects at the same time
- Communication
- Non-collection of billings, cash-flow
- Lack of focus in market strategy
- Interoffice procedures
- Time management
- Lack of structure
- Effectively applying team to all projects, from RFP through construction
- Getting the work done, faster
- Cost tracking and cost containment
- Lack of a plan for project quality

17 Project Management Tips from the Corps of Engineers

In a training program for its project managers, the Army Corps of Engineers asked the PMs what they had learned during recent projects. We thought the responses might prove instructive to A/Es working in the private (and public) sector.

1. Consider all the risks, and always have a backup plan.

2. Draw out the talents and ideas of the technical staff, and help them communicate.

3. Know what customers want, and communicate with them consistently.

4. Take time up front to build the team.

5. Get the project team on board and working together early.

6. Leave nothing to chance.

7. Be totally involved in the project.

8. Have a plan.

9. Put time, effort, and resources into defining project scope, and pick team leaders who have strong technical and (especially) people skills.

10. Manage your resources.

11. Hold customer (and in-house team member) feedback sessions throughout the course of the project, and make course corrections.

12. Use outside help to establish team support and communicate the need to build relationships.

13. Consider the customer as part of the team.

14. Ensure a good selection of contractors and types of contracts.

15. Don't count on in-house availability.

16. A balanced PM (emotionally and physically fit) can accomplish more than a strung-out, burned-out, overly aggressive PM.

Lessons learned should be incorporated in all future projects.

Controlling Project Studies and Reports

Study projects appear simple but present many unique challenges. The projects usually involve smaller teams, are shorter in duration, and have less defined scope of services than many design projects. This causes many firms to ignore them from a project management point of view until it's too late. Because the scope of work is more typical of R&D efforts, there is more risk to the firm if good management techniques are not imposed on these study efforts.

- Make sure you link the level of effort directly to the contract scope and fee. There is real danger in estimating the level of effort to complete a study if it's not tied directly to the contract scope and fee. There is always a tendency to provide clients with what the firm believes they need, not what the client is willing to pay for.

- Complete the data entry effort in the field. Provide laptop computers or other electronic means to input the data while the team is at the field site.

- Build an annotated report outline before you start writing the text of the report. Issue the report outline to the project team and client at the very beginning of the project.

- Include a preliminary table of contents, list of tables, figures, etc. Then include the format and style for the text and all enclosures and attachments.

- Never issue any report without conducting a peer review. The technical peer review provides the quality control for the study project and final report. Schedule periodic peer reviews during the project. Allow time in the budget and schedule to complete them and incorporate comments.

Simplify Your Filing System

Have you ever tried to locate a document in your project files and been frustrated because nothing was in the correct folder? Perhaps your filing system is just too complex.

One project manager we know has solved this problem by adapting the KISS principle (Keep It Simple Silly) to his filing system.

For most jobs, he has just one filing category, and everything gets filed chronologically based on the date of the document. (This also ensures that every document is dated.)

For large jobs, he sets up three file categories:

> incoming,
>
> outgoing, and
>
> internal.

Within each of these categories, everything is filed chronologically.

He tells us that this system has the following advantages compared to the traditional breakdown of files by document type:

- Less time is spent explaining to the team how to file documents.

- There is no need to make multiple copies to include in various categories, which often overlap.

- There are virtually no misfiled documents.

- It's easier to find filed documents because you generally know approximately when the document was sent or received.

The Ten Biggest Project Delivery Sins

Here are the ten ways to make sure your client never comes back to you for another project:

1. **Project team changes.** While clients understand planned changes in personnel between the different phases of the project (from programming to design development and construction), the core group of personnel should remain relatively unchanged. Particularly during the later phases, changes can cause considerable friction because the client has developed a comfort level with the established team. With ongoing relationships covering multiple projects, a consistent team becomes more important.

2. **Multiple A/E team contacts for the client representative.** Clients want few points of contact, since dealing with numerous team members makes their job more difficult. Few individuals should have direct contact with the primary client representative. The remainder of the design team is a resource, available as needed. This strategy allows for a close working relationship to develop with a high level of support, and it avoids an internal conflict regarding project management roles.

3. **Schedule delays and missed milestones.** When the design team falls behind during design, the client bears the burden of having to either make decisions faster or compress the construction schedule to meet a desired completion date. In the

client's mind, both of these options require energy and added cost—and may lead to future problems.

4. **Over-design.** Often, this approach takes the form of "thinking in the client's best interest," which is an egotistical view. Although the design team may often have more knowledge than the client, the team needs to educate the client through communication rather than making decisions for the client.

5. **Negative approaches to problems.** Contractors make mistakes and often make the project difficult for the design team; however, the client wants solutions to problems, not conflict among the project team members. This approach relies not on making the construction team infallible but on working with the team where possible and avoiding negative communication. Instead of looking to the specification to solve problems and conflicts, you should take a more practical approach is needed. One reason for the popularity of partnering and design/build is the continuing need for a problem-solving approach that addresses all the client's needs.

6. **Low-quality product.** Quality is low when the plans and specs result in multiple bid addenda and a large number of change orders. Clients have come to expect very few changes from design errors, especially those due to insufficient research or poor design. Changes slow the project and add cost. When combined with #3 above, repeat business from the client is doubtful at best.

7. **Slow response to construction questions.** Whether questions are asked informally or via written request, the speed with which they are answered has a large impact on the pace of the project. Clients often see an inverse relationship between construction questions and the quality of construction documents. A slow response from the design team in answering questions only exacerbates the problem.

8. **Slow review of submittals.** This is often an area of considerable conflict as subcontractors can be slow with submittals and the design team becomes overwhelmed at a critical juncture in the project. However, the time allotted by the specifications is irrelevant to the client since the client's goal is to keep the project moving forward. A number of strategies will mitigate this problem while maintaining leadership and control; one approach is to schedule the submittals.

9. **Weak leadership.** Contrary to popular belief, the design team has a vital role in all phases of the project. From the origin of the project through completion, quality and client interests suffer without a strong design team. In the absence of strong leadership from the design team, the general contractor/ construction manager drives the project, and the client begins to consider the design service (and product) in commodity terms.

10. **Absence at final completion.** The period between substantial and final completion is critical for the client. Design and construction problems must be

brought to a resolution simultaneously with the startup and operation of building systems. The design team can increase client satisfaction by remaining involved during this period to ensure successful startup of systems and training of building staff. This approach enhances the high level of service provided throughout the project. Continuing involvement creates a relationship with facilities management and provides the client with resources other than the trade contractors and general contractor/ construction manager to bring the project to a successful final completion.

Keep Material Substitutions Under Control

The best way to avoid problems in the bid phase of a project is through using standardized procedures for review. Reduce the likelihood of substitutions by making your original selections carefully.

- Involve the owner in material and product selection.

- Don't propose products the owner can't afford.

- Make sure the products specified will be available when needed and can be delivered on time.

- Use your specification options wisely:
    - A closed specification restricts the contractor to products and manufacturers listed.

- An open specification allows the contractor to provide other manufacturers.

To control substitutions after the award of the contract, provide these guidelines in the supplementary conditions:

- A request must be accompanied by complete data on the proposed substitution.

- Permission to submit substitutions is not to be construed as "pre-approval" in any sense.

- Requests for substitution, when forwarded by the contractor to the project manager are understood to mean the contractor:
  - Has investigated the proposed substitute.
  - Will provide the same guarantee as for the specified product.
  - Has included all cost data and waives any future costs.
  - Will coordinate the installation.

- The engineer or architect will record all time spent in evaluating proposed substitutions. Whether the A/E approves the substitution or not, the contractor shall pay for the A/E's services through the owner.

When evaluating a proposed substitution:

- Review the proposed changes with the firm's materials review committee or a senior partner.

- Remember that the owner makes the final decision.

- Keep track of your time spent in evaluation and bill all time to the contractor through the owner.

- Find out why the substitution has been proposed.

- Use concrete reasons when rejecting a proposal:
  - Cannot match specified capacities, size, insulating value, etc.
  - Gauges of metal are thinner than specified.
  - Not available in desired color or finish.
  - Requires more energy to operate.

- Don't go it alone when evaluating a product or material substitution. Consult with everyone who could be affected. Formulate a basis of opinion based on the individuals consulted.

- Don't be intimidated into accepting a substitute, and use common sense.

Identifying "Red Flags" to Project Failure

Here's a list of common issues that may arise during projects. If you encounter any of these red flags, there is a good chance that you are headed down a path towards project failure.

- The client is not returning your calls.

- The client begins questioning hours on the invoice.

- The client starts asking for more detailed back-up on work accomplished.

- Schedules begin slipping.

- Your are trying to work additional scope into original budgets.

- Percent spent begins to be greater than percent complete.

- No project management plan has been completed for the project.

- The client seems surprised at decisions being made.

- You do not use an Action Item List to track actions or assignments for the project team.

- You are surprised by the number of hours team members are charging to the project.

- You have a higher-than-normal number of new or untrained staff on your project team.

- You have higher-than-normal turnover of staff on your project team.

- You or your project team are not familiar with your firm's published QA/QC policies.

- Senior management is not involved in project development and review until late in the project.

- Subcontractor or subconsultant is new to working with your company.

- Subcontractors and subconsultants are not meeting schedules for intermediate project milestones.

- You are not monitoring your project progress with the 3-line graph.

- Project logistics such as jobsite access, weather, and local permitting requirements are not addressed during project planning.

- Change orders have not been documented or communicated in writing to the client.

- Project includes a new design or construction technology.

- Every deliverable is met only after a great flurry of last-minute activity and effort.

- A new client project manager is brought in to complete the project.

Don't get blindsided with unwanted surprises! Keep an eagle eye on your projects and look out for any red flags that could lead to bigger problems later on in the project.

CHAPTER 10

GETTING OUT OF TROUBLE

What's Going Wrong with My Project?

While it is essential to know the budget and schedule status of a project at a given point in time, monitoring trends can be even more revealing If you find that your schedule is consistently losing ground every month, you should look for the reasons that might be causing it.

Possible explanations include:

- You have underestimated the amount of time required to do the project.
- The staff on the job are not working efficiently.
- Other projects you are involved in are interfering with your ability to focus on this one.
- The client may be holding you up by not providing input as requested.
- You aren't able to get the staff levels you need on the project.

- You are spending too much time trying to resolve details.

- You are examining too many design alternatives.

Also, watch out also for sudden changes in the budget status in one, or a succession of, reporting periods. If you find that your budget suddenly develops major problems in one month it may be because:

- The client could have requested extra work, which your team subsequently performed, and you did not adjust your budget accordingly.

- You had a sudden influx of staff on your project that was not effective.

- You could have underestimated some direct costs on your project.

- You may have discovered an error and had to rework part of the project to make the necessary corrections.

- Costs have been charged to your project incorrectly.

Monitoring trends in your budget and schedule status can be useful to see where your project is heading in the long run. But it's only effective if you monitor the project on a regular and frequent basis. Irregular or infrequent reporting will not accurately show the trends of your project status.

Attack Project Issues with Brainpower

Brainstorming is more than a verbal free-for-all in which everyone speaks until a brilliant idea suddenly emerges. Conducted properly, it is an orderly process that leads to sound conclusions with a minimum of wasted effort.

When your team is faced with a complex problem or roadblock on a project, you may want to consider setting up a brainstorming session and include the following phases:

1. **Objective definition.** Define the objective of the brainstorming session. Is it to develop a measurement technique, determine the root cause of a problem, or identify the best solution? If the objective of the session is not clearly understood, the discussion will meander along many blind alleys.

2. **Solicitation of ideas.** During this phase, you should solicit ideas from all team members. Any ideas related to the objective are welcomed and written on a blackboard for all to see. Do not permit any discussion of the merits of ideas during this phase. Your goal is to encourage everyone to present their ideas, and build on previously presented ideas.

3. **Screening.** At this point, each idea should be discussed. Those that are duplications should be combined. Those that obviously hold no promise should be eliminated from further consideration. In most brainstorming sessions, this screening

process should reduce the number of ideas by 50 to 75%.

4. **Prioritization.** The remaining ideas should be prioritized to determine which ones deserve further study. One way of doing that is by "multi-voting." For the first vote, each person selects the best half of the list of ideas (for example, if there are 12 ideas on the list, each person gets 6 votes).

The next step in the multi-voting process is the "ten/four vote." Each person gets a total of ten votes to cast, with no more than four votes for any single idea. The written secret ballots are then counted and prioritized accordingly.

5. **Homework assignments.** If the session is unable to totally meet the meeting's objective, it may be necessary to set individual assignments to be completed prior to the next meeting.

6. **Documentation.** It is essential that you fully document all results and distribute them to every participant involved.

9 Ways to Overcome Problems on Your Project

No matter how carefully you plan your project and protect yourself against the possibility of trouble, problems will arise. For example, you may fall behind schedule or run over budget.

What can be done to eliminate or reduce the number of problems?

1. **Pick the best solution, and go with it.** Every alternative you have developed is 90 percent perfect. But until you determine the final direction for the project, all the work on alternative solutions is wasted time and money. Pick the one that is guaranteed to work, and go with it.

2. **Only do what is required by the con**tract. Review the scope of the work, and make sure you are only doing those tasks that you are being paid for. If the client is insisting that you add to the scope, then you have every right to ask for additional fee and an extension of the schedule.

3. **Keep production on schedule.** If the schedule slips, bring in some outside help for a short period of time to get the production back to where it should be. You can borrow staff from another project or even from another firm that you work with. For nontechnical tasks, you can use clerical and administrative employees to do routine jobs.

4. **Make sure you are using the correct balance of experienced staff.** Too many beginners on the project make time and fee consuming mistakes that you can't afford when you are trying to get back on track. Senior people are much more productive if they don't have to spend time supervising trainees. Likewise, the project manager can do more technical work while eliminating supervisory time.

5. **Postpone non-critical administrative duties until the crunch is over.** Then spend the extra time on the most critical aspects of the project. (Don't over- use this technique—principals may tire easily of such requests.)

6. **Optimize your production techniques.** Do you use CAD or reprographic tricks to reduce the time it takes to finish the set? Make sure your best people are working on CAD—they know the most advanced productivity techniques.

7. **Renegotiate consultant contracts.** If the total budget is in trouble, perhaps consultants are to blame. Review and renegotiate their contracts if necessary. Also, if some of the consultants' tasks will not be needed, eliminating them may save the project budget.

8. **Don't hide in your office doing paperwork.** As the PM, it's your job to be out there with the team focusing on the productive work of the project. The paperwork will wait until after you get back on schedule.

9. **Finally, have a talk with your client.** Instead of immediately asking for an extension, suggest ways in which the client can help achieve the target date, such as the use of client staff for certain tasks. The client may have access to resources that can help you, be willing to let certain activities slide until a later date, or even be willing to give you more time.

Review the project to see if the client has been the cause of any unnecessary delays. If so, you have every right to ask for an extension.

How to Avoid Crisis on Your Projects

Many say that the principal role of a project manager is to plan the work and work the plan. Done right, this approach factors out the possibility of crisis. Looked at from the troubleshooting side, then, the PM's task is to avert unnecessary crises and anticipate unavoidable ones.

How can you best take on this task and keep your projects out of trouble?

Philip Crosby, a well-known expert in quality improvement, stresses the value of early recognition of, and solutions to, quality problems. A problem that costs $1 to prevent will cost $10 if caught by the firm's internal review system—and $100 if caught by the contractor or client.

Assemble your team at the outset of every project and follow five steps for success.

1. With your team brainstorm the question, "What can go wrong that will hurt the quality of this project?"

2. List all responses on an easel pad or blackboard.

3. Discuss each possible problem, and ask for ideas that can prevent the problem or mitigate its impact.

4. Chart the results as shown in the table below.

5. Incorporate this list into the project management plan, and distribute it to all team members so they can prevent these problems or solve them before they become serious.

Better to spend a few hours up front preparing a crisis prevention plan than waste hundreds of hours later fixing a problem you could have avoided.

Potential Problems and Preventive Measures

1.) Easements and rights-of-way (ROWs) may be difficult to obtain. May cause a delay in design schedule.

- Establish detailed listing of all easements and ROWs; update their approval status every two weeks

- Set up early design review meetings with DOT personnel responsible for granting ROWs.

2.) Location of existing utilities may not be well-defined. This could generate an excessive number of change orders during construction.

- Hire surveyor to "pot hole" congested areas to locate existing utilities.

- Include an allowance for utility relocation required during construction.

3.) Older pipelines may not withstand pressure increase when the new system comes on line—and may result in line breakage.

- Request engineering change order from client to test existing lines.

- Owner should put all repair crews on 24-hour notice for one week after start-up of new system.

Some Not-So-Obvious Sources of Design Error

Construction cost growth is an insidious cancer that threatens our industry. In the area of public construction where highly visible, often controversial public works projects are delivered, a construction cost growth higher than about 5% is guaranteed to generate controversy, recriminations and can ultimately undermine the public's confidence in their government.

While there are several root causes of construction cost growth, including many that cannot be anticipated, design error is an obvious cause that should be avoided. Even with formal QC policies, plans, and procedures in place, embarrassing errors occur. Many policies are honored more in the breach than in fact.

1. **Incorrect or outdated design references and standards**. In many cases a plan assembly will refer to a standard without referencing the edition or date of the standard. In most cases, these standards are revised periodically, and the constructor should be expected to build to the

standard that the designer used to design the project. Some designers simply refer to the "latest edition." This is inadequate! The designer needs to reference the edition and/or date that was used as a basis for the design.

2. **Incorrect or differing datum.** The project datum is often taken for granted. The benchmark is located, referenced on the plan, and that is that. The purpose of a datum is to locate a project in space, both horizontally and vertically. This location is used to relate the project to other terrain features in the vicinity. The designer needs to be sure that the datum is identified and that the datum and adjacent terrain features are located on the same datum.

3. **Stale plans.** Owners and agencies will often develop a set of plans for a project and for whatever reason, the plans will sit on a shelf for a period of time before they are let for construction. Meanwhile, life has moved on. The terrain can change, adjacent land use can change, utilities may have moved. In a rapidly growing area, major changes can occur in a surprising short period of time. Thus, if a plan assembly is allowed to sit on a shelf prior to release, a final QC review including an extensive field review is in order.

4. **Field conditions vary from design assumptions.** Designers work in an office environment. Projects are delivered in the field. Designers will typically do a site visit at the start of the project, then may not visit the site ever again. The designer will

base the design on surveys, aerial photos, the initial site visit and perhaps, an occasional, informal visit. In many cases the design assumptions are not adequate given the field realities. The design team must be disciplined to field check the design frequently during the design process.

As project manager, you play a role in mitigating and preventing these kinds of "hidden liabilities" from occurring.

Why Good Budgets Go Bad

The first step in controlling your costs is to recognize the typical "budget killers"—the common pitfalls that always lead to cost overruns.

The outline below shows typical cost problems and when they are likely to occur. Keep a close eye on these issues to ensure your budgets stay ship-shape.

Proposal phase problems

- Failure to understand each client's requirements.

- Unrealistic appraisal of in-house capabilities

- Underestimating time requirements

Planning phase problems:

- Omissions

- Inaccuracy of the task list or work breakdown structure

- Misinterpretation of information
- Use of incorrect estimating techniques
- Failure to identify and focus on major cost elements

Negotiation phase problems:

- Forcing a speedy compromise
- Procurement ceiling costs
- A "we need this job no matter what" negotiating attitude

Contractual phase problems:

- Contractual discrepancies
- Difference between scope of work and RFP
- A proposal team different from the project team

Design phase problems:

- Accepting client requests without management approval
- Problems communicating with the client
- Designers who won't stop designing

Production phase problems:

- Overdrawing
- Unnecessary changes
- Ineffective quality control and assurance procedures

Specification phase problems

- Providing material and product information too late
- Continual design changes
- Distributed authority for specification writing

9 Ways to Handle a Project that's Late

The deadline is fast approaching. What can you do to meet it? Here are nine ways to come in on time:

1. **Work overtime.** This is usually the first step in getting back on schedule. Remember, productivity is better on Saturday and Sunday, rather than working until midnight during the week.

2. **Change work assignments.** A problem may be the inappropriate assignments to staff members who may not be receiving adequate instructions. The solution may be to bring on new individuals with fresh drive to take over the problem and get the project back on track.

3. **Use temporary help.** Have a permanent list of temporary help, including retired employees or former staff members who could work a second shift. This will ensure that each temp will know your firm and will be productive when hired.

4. **Use principals.** Putting principals to work can take advantage of available experts, who generally charge time to your project anyway. An experienced professional may accomplish in one

hour what an in- experienced technician does in five.

5. **Reassess contingencies**. If your schedule has unrealistic contingencies built into it because you have assigned a 10 percent contingency factor to each task, you may actually be on schedule but not know it. Examine your schedule progress on a task-by-task basis.

6. **Involve the client**. Suggest ways in which the client could help you achieve the target date, possibly using the client's staff to perform certain appropriate tasks.

7. **Reorganize drawings**. Conduct a planning meeting with the CAD department. Use fewer sheets with less information on each, and omit elaborate details. Use more reprographic techniques, such as photocopying details or entire sections of a drawing. Eliminate hand-lettered notes where possible.

8. **Eliminate excess alternatives**. Examine your project closely to eliminate excessive research into alternatives.

9. **Implement performance specifications**. Require contractors to submit material specifications rather than writing them. Before using this technique, determine your firm's liability status and your contract with the owner.

Attempt all of the above before the last resort of asking the client for an extension. Clients don't like a firm that can't perform on time, especially if financing is contingent on your performance.

Can You Control Project Creep?

Project creep is when you find that your project is expanding to fill the available time of your staff. How do you control that? Here are some suggestions:

- Re-measure the size of your task assignments before they're assigned. Rather than thinking in "milestones," think in terms of "inch pebbles."

- Rather than giving your team members broad tasks on which they'll spend the next four weeks, give them more specific tasks, and manage them in shorter periods of time.

- Break apart your task assignments into smaller pieces that are monitored on an hourly basis rather than on a weekly basis.

It means more control by you, the project manager. It also means that you should spend more time walking around, checking the activities of each team member.

You can't afford to have projects expand by even 10 or 15 percent these days, or you'll lose your shirt on the project.

It's not a complex thing to do. Reduce your project assignments to smaller, more bite-sized pieces, and you'll control project creeping.

PM as Surgeon

When you find that a project fee or construction cost is projected to be "over budget," you have to put on your surgeon's gown.

A smart PM will use the following "surgical procedure:"

1. **Be dispassionate.** Don't get emotionally involved during the process. Be cool and professional.

2. **Take tests, diagnose.** Know the problem. Make sure there is a problem before you recommend action. Check for math errors in estimates, quantity take-off mistakes, unit material and/or labor prices that seem out of line.

3. **Count the pieces.** Make sure there are no redundancies in the estimate. Count everything once, but only once.

4. **Brainstorm.** If you really do have a budget problem, start a list of cost cutting ideas ranging from minor refinements to major changes.

5. **Be progressive.** When you cut, proceed by asking these questions:

   - How can I save cost without reducing scope or lowering quality? (e.g., different procurement strategies.)

   - Where are the opportunities to postpone or shift costs? (e.g., have the owner perform some work out of a maintenance budget, rather than project construction budget.)

- Are there ways to add quality later? (e.g., build all the scope now, add improved finishes later.)

- Only after the above have been considered should you cut scope and/or quality.

6. **Spread the problem.** Ask each discipline to come up with ten percent cost reductions.

7. **Involve the patient.** Let the client be aware of all of your activities.

8. **Get paid.** When a project is over budget, it is not necessarily your fault. Make sure you request and receive additional services compensation when you implement cost cutting or value engineering services.

Don't Let the Budget Unravel

The last thing you can afford is a budget that continually grows out of proportion to its original estimation. Keep tight control of your budgets by actively following these eight steps:

1. **Set realistic initial budgets.** Don't fool yourself. Make initial budget allocations compatible with the scope of work expected.

2. **Include a contingency plan.** Don't be overly optimistic. Recognize that there will be unforeseen conditions and minor changes for which you can't request additional compensation. We suggest five percent of total fee.

3. **Make honest percent-complete estimates.** Don't rely on job-cost reports. Double-check estimates, and check at every "additional 10 percent complete" milestone.

4. **Use trend analysis.** Don't depend on today's status; look ahead. Consider "what if" options based on current or revised staffing, schedule, design objectives, quality requirements, and client expectations.

5. **Take corrective action at the first sign of trouble.** Don't think the problem will correct itself.

6. **Start only what you know you can finish.** Don't overestimate what you can get done. If you've started drawings or specifications which can't be completed within budget, find an alternative way to complete them.

7. **Have a strict additional services procedure.** Don't give away services. Establish an additional services review and approval procedure. Inform team members that there is no compensation for additional services performed without your prior approval.

8. **Take non-performers off your job.** Identify those who are just killing time and move them along.

Balancing Time, Cost, and Performance

Time, cost, and performance—that's the magic combination every project manager pursues. If a project were to flow perfectly, there would be no need for trade-offs between these elements. Unfortunately, the project without crisis has yet to be completed and every project manager must balance time versus cost versus performance.

Trade-offs are always based on the constraints of the project, and all projects have an underlying—if not overt—constraint structure. Most projects work under the constraints of fixed time and cost, while performance is variable. Many environmental projects work with performance fixed, while time (and sometimes cost) is variable. You must understand the constraints in your projects to evaluate and decide on trade-offs.

The following checklist can be useful in evaluating your projects:

Time

- ❏ Is a time delay acceptable to the client?
- ❏ Will the time delay change the completion date for other projects and other clients?
- ❏ What is causing the time delay?
- ❏ Can resources be recommitted to meet the new schedule?
- ❏ What will be the cost of the new schedule?
- ❏ Will the increased time give added improvement?
- ❏ Will an extension of this project cause delays on other projects in the client's organization?
- ❏ What will the client's response be?

❑ Will the increased time change our learning curve?

❑ Will this hurt our firm's ability to win future work?

Cost

❑ What is causing the cost overrun?

❑ What can be done to reduce remaining costs?

❑ Will the client accept an additional charge?

❑ Should we absorb the extra cost?

❑ Can we renegotiate the time or performance standards to stay within costs?

❑ Are the projected costs for the remainder of the project accurate?

❑ Will there be any net value gains for the increased funding?

❑ Is this the only way to satisfy performance?

❑ Will this hurt our company's ability to procure future contracts?

❑ Is this the only way to maintain schedule?

Performance

❑ Can the original performance standard be met?

❑ If not, at what cost can we guarantee compliance?

❑ Is the performance standard negotiable?

❏ What are the advantages to the firm and the client if the performance standard is changed?

❏ What are the disadvantages?

❏ Are we increasing or decreasing performance?

❏ Will the client accept a change?

❏ Will liability be incurred?

❏ Will the change in performance cause a redistribution of project resources?

❏ Will this hurt the firm's ability to win future work?

Overcoming Over-Budget Problems

Following are some ways to overcome budget problems and get back on track:

- **Examine the figures**. Before making any changes, be sure that you're really over budget. Check all charges of time and expenses to your project. Ask your financial manager for a current assessment of your overhead charges to be certain that all charges have been made as planned when the project was budgeted.

- **Check to be sure that everything you're doing is** required in the scope of work. If something is not, stop work, or get additional funding from the client.

- **Examine each task**. Be sure that only experienced people are working on those activities requiring judgment and only junior people are working on tasks that merely require persistence.

- **Shorten the schedule and work overtime**. This will reduce coordination costs by minimizing the number of people working on the project. It will also cut overhead costs because overtime hours do not carry the same burden as regular hours.

- **Stop evaluating alternative solutions**. Go with what you know will work, and don't change your mind unless someone can convince you that what you have selected won't work.

- **Renegotiate consultant contracts**. If the total budget is in trouble, perhaps other consultants caused aspects of the problems. If so, you may be justified in renegotiating their contracts. Also, if some of the consultants' tasks will not be needed, eliminating them may save a project budget.

- **Use temporary help**. The firm can save payment of some fringe benefits by issuing temporary help. At current figures of 20 percent of direct labor, major budget savings could be made if the temporary help is able to produce right away on a project.

- **Be a squeaky wheel**. If your project is over budget, don't hide it. If you inform everyone in the firm that you are in trouble, those (such as principals) who might otherwise charge a random hour to your project will think twice. If you can save even one hour per week, it may be the difference between profit and loss.

- **If all else fails, ask the client for a budget or fee increase.** If the scope or other circumstances have changed, don't be afraid to go back and ask for more. Even if he or she says no, you have at least informed the client that you are closely watching changes. This could discourage the client from calling with nickel-and-dime changes. Also, you may get the added money if your request is legitimate and the client likes the work you are doing.

How to Improve Project Profitability

The amount of available work during the past few years has distracted many design firms from the basics of project profitability. With an abundance of work, it is often easier to make up for past losses with future fees than to correct project management problems causing the losses in the first place. Now is the time to fix your project management procedures before project losses multiply into firm losses.

Existing Projects

Here are the steps to take to shore up your existing projects:

- **Find out where all projects stand.** Ask each project manager to list all tasks left to do on existing projects and to estimate the hours left to complete each task.

- **Estimate all fees still to be collected on each project.** Then compare "work left" to "fee still due." Develop a list of projects that need your immediate attention.

- **Finish up design work.** More money is lost on projects by allowing designers to continue designing despite schedules or budgets. Stopping excessive perfectionism can improve profits quickly.

- **Clamp down on uncompensated changes.** Hold a meeting on each project, and review your client agreement with the entire project team. Explain what a "free" change is and when to charge for a change.

- **Attack "elastic" hours.** When work slows, tasks can mysteriously fill the available time. Have each project manager tell those doing a task exactly how long they have to get it done. Toughen delegation.

- **Collect fees or stop work.** Avoid situations where seven designers are working on a project and no invoices are being paid. Before stopping work, advise your client in writing with a stern and contractually legal warning. Then stop!

- **Accelerate project schedules, even if you must work overtime.** Shorter schedules produce more profitable projects because less time is wasted on the design. When possible, accelerate the schedule and you'll save money.

New Projects

With all new projects, start off correctly by taking these steps:

- **Set up a tough budget and schedule, in writing—** before starting any work. Even for undefined hourly work, set a due date and target a number of hours for any task.

- **Get tough on contract language.** Every new contract should contain: a stop work clause, a restart fee provision if work is stopped, automatic fee increases for work beyond a certain date, limits on liability, and procedures for payment to you on charges initiated by a client or outside agency not under your control. The single biggest cause of poor project profit is usually a badly written contract. Don't just sign a standard association form. Put teeth into each new contract.

- **When possible, never begin working drawings until design decisions are final.** One cause of project losses is repeatedly doing over working drawings.

- **Increase client reviews.** Don't let projects go on for weeks or months without client reviews. Otherwise, you may have to change even more drawings.

- **Plan a kickoff meeting on all projects.** Bring each client into your office for a meeting with everyone on the project. The objective is to have your team fully understand why the client is doing the project, what the expectations are, what quality is needed, and how critical the budget/schedule is. The more your staff understands the client's point of view, the more likely you are to have a profitable project.

The message here is to refocus your attention on what has made your firm so successful—profitable projects. Start by meeting with your project managers to attack unprofitable activities that could cripple your firm in the future.

How to Ensure Poor Profitability

Since on average, 70 percent of a design firm's total payroll goes into labor spent working on projects, how well each project is managed is the major determinant of a firm's profitability. Successful firms must control the man-hours needed to complete the work and to continually assess the probability of overruns in time to prevent them.

Utilization is Not the Key to Profitability

Each man-hour charged to a client is not necessarily profitable just because of the multiplier used to establish billing rates. That man-hour, if it is in excess of the time that the project should have taken, diminishes the project's contribution to overhead and profit. In effect, the man-hour and its cost are a loss.

If the man-hour overrun is mistakenly included in direct charges to projects, it distorts utilization. You'll then agonize about how profitability could be so low when everyone is so busy.

You'll wonder if overhead is getting too high, but your fears appear groundless because the same high direct-labor charges caused by overruns are keeping the overhead rate well within bounds. You'll then take a look at the net effective multiplier which has taken a beating and, rather than finding out why, decide your profit problems are the fault of the market's competitiveness or the clients' reluctance to pay enough for your services.

Watch for these Red Flags of financial failure:

- **High work-in-process.** It postpones the day when the project manager discovers his/her project is incurring more man-hours than were planned. It disguises an overrun, usually at billable rates, as an asset and not a loss.

- **Low receivables turnover.** When the client holds up payment for man-hours spent on work performed in the distant past, the invoice becomes suspect, and you lose even more time proving it valid.

- **A low effective multiplier.** It reveals some or all of the following problems:

  - The principal felt the project important enough to obtain, regardless of the man-hour budget.

- The man-hour budget was set up after the fee was agreed on.

- The man-hours needed were established as a percentage of the fee and ignored the time needed to get the work done.

- The work was planned before the fee was agreed upon, but the project manager neither calculated the average base man-hour cost of the project team nor used the firm's net effective multiplier goal when negotiating the fee.

- The project manager erroneously considered the man-hour budget padded, so artificially cut the budget during fee negotiation.

- The project manager, recognizing the reality of the client's fee for the job, failed to assess the degree to which the "working budget" could be reduced to attain the net effective multiplier target.

- The project manager failed to provide either the subcontractors or the client with a clear understanding of the scope needed to meet the client's quality standards.

All of these problems result in projects heading for a substandard net effective multiplier before the work is even begun. Overruns are unavoidable at the outset.

Hold Monthly Reviews

To avoid these problems, start checking the net effective multiplier on each project at least once a month. Such a review should reveal:

- An unrealistic estimate of man-hours to complete the work.

- Poor productivity.

- Untrained project team members who are not clear about the scope of work they are to perform or the method intended when the man-hour budget was established.

- Use of more highly paid people than needed or planned for.

- Failure to agree on the man-hour budget with those assigned to the work.

- Tendency to "gold plate," i.e., doing more than the standard of quality the client actually expects and agreed to in the contract.

- Internal re-work to meet quality standards.

- Work performed gratuitously beyond the scope agreed to.

- Re-work caused when client or firm changed its mind about the design or design criteria. The added work is then performed free or for an inadequate fee that lowers the net effective multiplier.

- Failure to re-budget work packages or tasks included in the project as soon as the budget has become unrealistic.

- Too many staff on project teams or excess overtime when agreed schedules are in jeopardy.

In conclusion, high utilization and low overhead rates, though good indicators, will not guarantee high profitability. But high overruns will ensure poor profitability and, perversely, distort the accuracy of the other two measures of effectiveness.

How to Control Project Costs

By following a risk-minimizing process, the design professional can control project costs.

We all like to believe that we have control over such costs. After all, our clients expect us to exercise our professional judgments in developing a realistic project budget. They further expect that when the bids are received, one or more of these bids will be within this budget.

Needless to say, we know that the outcome will vary from client to client, project to project, and bid to bid.

How is the budget determined? Generally, the project budget is established by factoring costs from previous projects and the use of estimating guides that determine dollars-per-square-foot costs. This budget may be developed prior to, during, or at the end of design.

At times, construction management consultants are in to assist in developing the budget. It is then used by the client to get funding approval. Once the project is approved, it's put out for bid.

What happens during bidding? What one perceives as a linear, predictable process can become chaotic and beyond control. Why? Because bids may be prepared on an entirely different set of assumptions; they may be made in response to market conditions that are not reflected in estimating guides or databases from previous projects.

Bid factors might include:

- The number of contractors bidding on the project.
- The bidders' level of experience in your project type.
- The number of projects that were bid the week before.
- The availability of the labor pool to do the work.
- The availability of an experienced foreman to supervise the installation.
- The availability of materials, etc.

How to Minimize your Risk

It's difficult to maintain a great deal of control in unforeseen circumstances, such as changes in the market.

The best way to handle these situations is to take proactive steps to minimize your risk:

The Pre-design Report

The pre-design report is the key to the process, addressing the who, why, what, when, and where questions that exists for every project. All too often we (and our clients) rush ahead without having a clear vision of the project. Concerns over a design that best takes into account cost, schedule, and client needs (which are not always mutually inclusive) may not be fully addressed early on. This leads to a change dilemma once the construction documents are completed.

The pre-design report is a mental exercise in design, with a minimal amount of drawing work. For a small expense, alternatives can be studied, problems identified and resolved, schedules reviewed, and budgets established. The ideal report will include one or more solutions, with corresponding and a schedule identified.

The report can be used by your client's management to: choose the solution that works best for them, secure project funding for the project, and confirm the schedule. When the client gives approval, you have a clear direction in which to proceed.

If you don't already use a pre-design report, you'll be surprised by how much clients appreciate it. They feel it gives them more involvement in the process, which makes your job easier and reduces your risks for budget, schedule, and redesign problems.

Professional Cost Estimating

Cost estimators are generally full-time professionals. Since cost estimating represents a small portion of the design professional's total responsibility, it's important that we have a clear understanding of how this process works.

We must know the order-of-magnitude cost to provide an appropriate design and to guide us in determining our fee. This magnitude of cost may not be accurate enough to reflect the final design and project phasing, but it must reflect the costs associated with a difficult installation and must include existing industry conditions at bid time.

Professional cost estimators fall into two categories: contractors and cost consultants. Both can be used to establish the budget for your design. Each has advantages and disadvantages.

Contractors must do cost estimating to secure their work and, to some degree, profit from it. At the time of bidding, they provide a design's market value. When they bid your project, they usually have a completed design to work from and are responding to the current market conditions.

Cost consultants carry a number of different labels: from construction managers to professional cost estimators. They use their years of experience and databases to determine a design's cost. To determine budgets, they use a combination of per-square-foot costs and itemized take-offs.

The accuracy of their budgets is only as dependable as the data and experiences they are basing them on. You'll find that professional cost estimators, either contractors or consultants, will enhance your team and allow for better bid results within the 5 (+ or -) percent range. The additional expense and effort to manage them will be well worth the results.

Quality Documents

Documents are probably the only item in the construction process over which the design professional has the most control. Work smart and use it wisely.

If the contractor is unable to determine what your design intent is, bidding on it and constructing it will be difficult. The detail and complexity of the documents will change depending on the delivery system employed (i.e., partnering, design-build, design-bid-build, etc.). The documents must always contain the information necessary for the contractor to bid the project and do the work.

Construction Administration

Construction administration is the process that allows you to stay in control during the construction phase. So often, the design professional's involvement is reduced substantially during the project's most critical phase: the interpretation of your design and its actual construction.

Every project is unique. Your design is an interpretation of your client's needs, and your solution in response to the physical conditions that are present.

Unfortunately, construction documents cannot cover every aspect of the project. The contractor doesn't view the documents through your eyes and with your understanding. For this reason, it's in the best interest of the project that you be involved throughout all of its phases.

Such involvement is simple. Your responsibilities include:

- Preparing the construction schedule in joint cooperation with the contractor.
- Chairing weekly site meetings.
- Preparing the meeting agenda and publishing the notes.
- Performing a job site inspection with the contractor's foreman prior to each meeting.

Typical agenda items in the construction site meeting include:

- A review of progress (based on the design professional's observations).
- Work that will be performed that week; status of schedule and necessary modifications.
- Resolution of problems from the last meeting that haven't been resolved.
- New issues.
- Scheduling of shut-downs that will occur during the week.

It's important that the client, the contractor's project manager, and all foreman are present at these meetings.

The purpose of this process is not to actually have you manage the construction. The contractor is still responsible for all contractual obligations. You are merely maintaining active involvement in the project to ensure that your client's needs are being met.

As design professional you must ensure that you're available whenever design questions arise—which they will.

How to Avoid Cost Overruns

The PM's essential financial responsibility is to earn the budgeted profit on projects. Project cost overruns cannot become typical of a project manager's performance. Consider the following ways to avoid overruns:

1. **Carefully define project scopes of work**. Only work that is directed toward the achievement of client objectives and covered by a contract should be performed. Plan this carefully, and communicate scope limits to the team.

2. **Correctly budget the project**. Eagerness to secure a project can lead to over-optimism about abilities to perform. Don't forget about review and correction time and normal work inefficiency.

3. **Understand your firm's project management reporting system**. Information is necessary for management of projects. Learn to read the

standard reports. Get information often enough to correct situations before they result in insurmountable problems.

4. **Make sure that financial information is correct and up to date.** Make sure your team correctly fills out time sheets and submits them on schedule. Encourage subcontractors to submit their bills on a timely basis.

5. **Work toward securing the "right" staff for your project.** Don't employ overqualified, overpaid personnel on your job; and avoid paying for excess amounts of training costs for less experienced personnel. Accept responsibility for your projects. Be willing to be accountable for appropriate profitability.

How to Reduce Creeping Job Costs?

You're in the eleventh hour of the project and nearly over budget. Whatever you are going to do, you've got to do it fast!

- Here are some suggestions for reducing overhead costs:

- Eliminate paid overtime by having salaried people finish the job.

- Use daily time sheets rather than weekly ones.

- Keep a close watch on the distribution of the workload.

- Set a rule requiring hourly employees to ask for your authorization before committing to any overtime.

10 Reasons to Charge More for Changes

Are you getting compensated fairly for the changes your clients expect you to make? Be sure you price the changes high enough to account for all of the extra costs! Here are a number of reasons why you should mark up changes using a standard, firm-wide percentage:

1. Changes negatively impact other clients by taking up additional time, resulting in potential damage to other projects.

2. Liability exposure increases because the chances are greater that the changes won't be made on all of your drawings.

3. Changes disrupt the project flow and may necessitate overtime work.

4. Each change is a small job on its own, and there's more overhead created by small projects.

5. You are saving the client money in the long run.

6. The changes improve the quality of the job, particularly if they are requested by the client.

7. Yours is the most capable firm to perform the changes—it's the most familiar with the project.

8. You need to charge more to recover overtime rates.

9. The markup can serve as a penalty for client-initiated changes and can be used to discourage them from making too many.

10. The changes impact the schedule. What's the cost to get the changes completed and still maintain the schedule?

A "Restart Fee" Avoids Losing Money

A/E/Cs have had experiences with projects that, for a variety of reasons, are stopped in mid-stream and then started again later. Few design firms collect for the loss resulting from such delays.

When projects are put on hold for more than 30 days, teams are disbanded, drawings shelved, and in extreme cases, design criteria are modified radically.

You can avoid losing money in such situations by including a clause in all contracts, establishing a minimum restart fee, specified in dollars or a percentage of the base fee, when a project is stopped for more than 30 days. Such a clause is no cost to your client unless the project is stopped, in which case you deserve the fee.

Stop "Excess Perfection Syndrome"

Many technical professionals don't know when to stop designing—a costly trait commonly known as "excess perfection syndrome" (E.P.S.). This results in your team doing more than is really necessary on a task; more than your firm negotiated to provide when you set your price.

Defining a Level of Excellence

In the early stages of a task, increased effort translates into increased quality and excellence. But as the task approaches 90 percent perfection, the work rapidly reaches the point of diminishing returns. At that point, you lose money in the form of work hours, with little real improvement.

It is your job to ask, "What level of excellence is really needed?" In the conceptual stages, maybe only 80 percent is necessary, while for a complex structural system, 98 percent or higher may be needed. One thing is certain— it's never possible to achieve 100 percent perfection.

Less than 100 percent perfection doesn't mean poor quality control and liability claims. On the contrary, it can mean reallocating resources for more quality control. For example, you might cut the designer off at 90 percent and use the remaining fee for the checkers to catch the mistakes.

Setting Limits in the Contract

One way to battle E.P.S. is through working out the level of quality in negotiations. For example, you might agree to provide three design options, with any beyond that requiring an additional fee:

Setting Limits for Your Team

With today's technologies, design professionals can design more and faster. But they typically kill any productivity gains technology affords, as the ease of integrating changes tempts designers to keep tweaking. Endless "finishing touches" can take a big bite out of expected profit.

Remember this when you decide to charge less for a design because the original draft takes less time. Without control, your technology rarely saves time!

Setting Limits for Yourself

PMs are just as guilty of excess perfection. Take this example:

A project manager studying the feasibility of installing snowmaking equipment at a ski area needs to know the difference in elevation between the lake and the top of the mountain. He sends a survey crew to level up and down the mountain. They close within a tenth of a foot and charge the project $2,000. They could have looked at a U.S. Geological Survey map and charged the project $10.

How to Salvage Your Profit When the Client Delays the Projects

The best way to handle stoppage of work is to include cancellation and delay clauses in your contract. It is not uncommon for developer projects to be suspended or even cancelled after early stages of the project have already been completed. You need to protect your firm, and the best time to approach the client about project delays is after you have been awarded the contract. During negotiations, include a clause in the contract that addresses both suspension of work and cancellation of work.

For a Suspension of Work ...

Include contract terms that require demobilization and remobilization charges in case of a suspension of work. Clients need to understand that when they delay work on a project for and extended time, firms always incur extra costs when moving the team off the project. Also, when team members return to a project after a lengthy duration, they can't be expected to jump right in where they left off: memories fade, and there is a reorientation process that demands time and money.

In addition, if a delay stretches into a new fiscal year, your project staff may have been given raises; labor costs may have risen; or you may charge higher fees. You need to consider these escalation factors when drafting the remobilization clause in your contract.

So how much should you charge? There is no easy way to estimate this, but D'Alessandro recommends charging a percentage of your overall fee.

For a Cancellation of Work

Just like demobilization and remobilization clauses, you should develop a clause that states you will be paid a nominal amount to cover costs if a project gets pulled completely. Also, don't let a delayed project remain open indefinitely. At some point you have to cut bait. In your contract, specify a limit of time for an acceptable delay in your contract clause (e.g., six months). When you pull out of the project, your fee should equate to the established cancellation charge.

Asking your client to agree to extra charges will be a hard sell with some clients. There will be client organizations that push back on this. Ultimately, the issue shouldn't make or break a contract, but remember, there is absolutely no harm in asking.

How to Help Your PMs Avoid Mistakes on Small Projects

Successful projects require the right project manager for the job. However, there also some additional actions you can take that will enable your PMs to deliver a profit on every project.

- Give the PM full authority to manage and control the work. Principals have a tendency to commandeer projects on a regular basis. Be available to answer question, act as a guide, and then stay out of the way.

- A successful project achieves sensible expectations. Beware of perfectionism and the manager with only one personal performance standard. Encourage and channel creativity into useful activities. You don't want creativity at the nuclear plant controls.

- Be aware of overselling your services. Some puffery ("extensive experience," "fully knowledgeable," etc.) is okay, but avoid raising false expectations project managers and their teams cannot meet.

- Require PMs to document each significant project event in a clear, timely manner. Ask them to try writing to a sixth grade level of understanding. Distinguish fact from opinion. Include pertinent telephone conversations, meetings, field trips, and the like.

- Make sure your project manager helps set the project budget and any revisions. Have the project manager prepare the technical (scope) section. The worst thing you can do is leave the PM out of the loop when negotiating the project budget and scope with the client.

- Speed of project management is critical, but double-edged. Talk to your PMs about instilling a sense of urgency in the staff. One author defined this as getting important things done in an acceptable manner at the lowest feasible cost in the shortest time. Insist on a working speed that does not create cost overruns or poor quality work. Sustained time pressures create stress and decrease productivity.

- Teach your PMs that quality assurance is inherent in a correctly managed project. Quality is doing the job right the first time. A major increase in quality will accrue from work task planning, providing enough work time, and checking the product before it goes out.

- Emphasize strict project budget control. Many professionals feel they must do a "perfect" job each time. They don't know when to stop, and overrun the budget. Replace chronic perfectionists—you can't afford them.

- Finally, understand that project management is directly correlated to the excess perfection curve.

Too much quality, as well as too little, is not cost effective. Choose techniques that work for you. Vest your project managers with the authority to manage, and hold them responsible for results. If you don't, another firm probably will.

Preventing Contractor Claims

Third-party claims brought against design consultants and their clients are frequently filed by contractors or other parties damaged by contractor error. You can help prevent these claims by offering a variety of services as part of your scope of services.

For example: Contractor pre-qualification helps ensure that the selected contractor has the experience and credentials required to perform the required services. That alone can help prevent problems. Moreover, should a problem arise, a reputable contractor will be more likely to seek a quick and equitable resolution.

Contractors that obtain work on an open bidding basis are sometimes unfamiliar with local conditions or the full scope of services that may be required, or they may be buying into a contract in hopes of making a profit through change orders and/or negligence claims.

Pre-bid meetings can help ensure contractors' questions are answered before work begins. You are in the best position to answer questions about your portion of the work.

Pre-construction meetings can further contribute to clear understanding between the contractors and design professionals involved in the project.

Construction observation services are essential to minimizing problems. The designer can spot problems that contractors, subcontractors, and other third parties do not see and can deal with them at the "molehill stage." The documentation that results can also help discourage a contractor from filing a suit for damages due to design firm negligence or omissions.

If an owner refuses your construction observation services, work with legal counsel to obtain contractual protection for claims that arise due to the lack of coordination of the construction documents during the construction phase.

You should call for the owner's agreement with the contractor to include a provision requiring the contractor to hold you and the owner harmless for jobsite safety. The same provision could call for the contractor to make you and the owner additional insurers on the contractor's general liability insurance.

Shop Drawing Review

A typical method used by unscrupulous contractors is to inundate design consultants with shop drawings, causing a sharp slowdown in the review process. Other problems can arise when shop drawings differ significantly from what was originally called for, but such differences are not highlighted.

You can use a contract provision to bring this problem to your client's attention, gaining client support in developing effective shop drawing review procedures. In essence, you identify which shop drawings you want to see, requiring the contractor to review and approve each drawing before you see it and call to your attention any that would represent a design change. By adhering to these requirements, you can help prevent shop drawing review from becoming a profit center for those who intend to misuse the process.

How to Eliminate Third-party Claims

Third-party claims account for nearly 40 percent of professional liability claims filed against architects and engineers. About half of these claims are filed by contractors. While design firms can avoid claims from clients through an effective contract formation process, most don't realize that the same contract can effectively reduce third-party claims as well.

To avoid these claims, you need to meet with your clients and explain how a number of contract provisions can lower your—and their—third-party liability exposure. That may be the only way through which some of the provisions will be accepted.

Five Ways to Avoid Claims

1) Include the contract in your report. When you are hired to conduct research and issue a report, third-parties are likely to rely on what you provide. To reduce your (and your client's) risk of being tagged "it," you could include a copy of the contract as an appendix to the report, to indicate specifically the scope of service involved and the nature of the agreement between yourself and the client.

2) Include third-party exclusion. Third-parties sometimes file a claim because, somehow, they think they are beneficiaries of the contract between you and your client. Putting a third-party exclusion in your general conditions will ensure that the agreement does not create any right or benefits for parties other than the consultant and the client.

3) Create measures to prevent contractor claims. Claims brought against owners and consultants are frequently filed by contractors, or by third-parties whose damages were caused by contractor error. Prevent these types of claims by offering a variety of services that should be included in your agreement's scope of services. Because these services will increase your client's short term expense, you have to educate your client about the long-term savings. Here are some examples:

- **Contractor prequalification** helps ensure that the contractor that is selected has the experience and reputation required to perform well. In turn, you are more likely to have the kind of relationship with such contractors that will make it easy to work out problems that do arise.

- **Pre-bid meetings** will help ensure that contractors' questions are answered and removes the gamesmanship that can otherwise occur.

- **Pre-construction meetings** solidify understandings with the contractor, so everyone knows when they will be needed and why.

- **Construction observation**—not just the occasional visits to the site—are essential. The construction observer can spot problems that others do not see, or can at least deal with problems while they are still in the "molehill" stage. The documentation that results discourages contractors from filing a suit, if only because it creates a "no-win" situation.

4) Get tough on shop drawings. In states where third-parties can sue for purely monetary losses, delay claims by contractors are becoming more common. Unscrupulous contractors will inundate consultants with shop drawings, causing a sharp slow-down in the review process. You can use a contract provision to bring this problem to your client's attention.

In essence, you should identify specifically which shop drawings you want to see, and require the contractor to review and approve each before you see it, and to call to your attention any that would represent a change.

5) Understand site safety issues. Claims filed against you by injured contractors' employees are among the most common of those not filed by clients or contractors.

In order to forestall these suits, and to permit you to reduce or eliminate any contingency allowance you should include in contemplation of the risk, the client needs to make it clear in your agreement that you have nothing to do with construction site safety, or the means, methods, sequences, and operations of construction. These functions should be vested solely in the contractor or, the construction manager.

How to Use an EMU to Control Your Internal Costs

Cost control management is fundamental to determining every project's financial success. Good project cost control begets good project management. It starts with the establishment of your base budget of costs and expands to the monitoring of these costs and to decision-making criteria down the line.

Cost control can thus be set into three parts (called "EMU"):

Establishment of costs

Monitoring of costs

Use of the cost information in decision making

Cost evaluation as a management tool is relatively easy to implement because the data is basic in nature (everything has a cost), readily available, and—thanks to today's software—easy to track, maintain, and monitor.

Cost information is one of the few "hard fact" activities available to project delivery managers, and management can use this information to back up a difficult decision or provide the basis for a vital one. Rather than utilize a management process that's rooted on intuition (based on experience parameters), cost information provides the best avenue for project decision-making criteria. It is also useful to foster a proposed management position or bolster an existing one.

Following is a basic EMU cost control and management plan. We're assuming that this method is for an internal cost associated with your project costs, and not for the cost work associated with the project itself. But you should note that it's just as effective when preparing a full construction project cost as it is in doing an internal office expense cost study.

Establish the project cost parameters or budget. The most common method is through line-item budgeting. Prepare a detailed itemization of project costs, and then reduce each project item to a project cost. For example:

> Project Manager Cost is hours estimated x hourly cost (40 hrs x $50/hr = $2,000).
>
> CAD Time is hours estimated x hourly cost (40 hrs x $30/hr = $1,200).
>
> Secretarial Support Time is hours estimated x hourly cost (20 hrs x $20/hr = $400). By creating a detailed line-item review of the work items of the project, you have established the intended or "projected costs" for the project.

Monitor the costs. This is accomplished through weekly allocation from the accounting process of costs expended in each of the categories. Many firms use a cost control number and provide a cost code for each activity. Tracking by cost codes makes a uniform tracking method for the entire firm to use. For example:

> Cost Code 1000: Project Manager Cost is hours estimated x hourly cost (40 hrs x $50/hr = $2,000).

Cost Code 2000: CAD time is hours estimated x hourly cost (40 hrs x $30/hr = $1,200).

Cost Code 3000: Secretarial Support time is hours estimated x hourly cost (20 hrs x $20/hr = $400).

Use the data to make project decisions. The cost code and the line items provide one side, or axis, of the chart, while expended costs provide the other chart axis. For this activity, a simple graphing chart or computer spreadsheet can be utilized for the task.

With this simple (EMU) management device, you can establish your project budget and the project costs to target for review. By paying attention to costs, you can monitor the financial health of your endeavor.

If the information is timely and the costs extend over a long enough period, you'll have the tools to make a decision on adding resources for the project's financial success.

Once again, this same method is also effective in monitoring project costs for the construction process. As a matter of fact, the design-build approach depends greatly on this information to control the variable costs of design. Extended further, it is necessary to monitor and control the cost of the work itself.

CHAPTER 11

CONSTRUCTION ADMINISTRATION

Lessons Learned to Avoid Crisis During Construction

Many of the typical problems that arise during construction can be prevented with the right approach. PSMJ Resources consultant Michael D'Alessandro, PE, PMP, offers five tactics for a claims-free project:

1. **Promote the policy of "single statement."** If you are providing information in a drawing specifications package, state that information one time and don't repeat it in different drawings. For example, the dimensions of a room may change but you may not remember to change the redundant information on other drawings. This can open you up to claims and increase construction cost. State information one time, otherwise you invite conflict.

   Of course, there are times where you will be directed by agencies to repeat redundant information. In this case, you need to have a conversation with the plan review agency about the dangers of this. In a politically sensitive manner, say "What you are asking us to do violates best practices." Don't push the subject if they persist, but do let them know the situation.

2. **Deliver the minimum design necessary to get the project built without excess cost growth during construction.** Designers sometimes forget that drawing is not the end product, but the vehicle to get to the end (the building). The goal is to get the project built, so don't waste time on excess detail; it's usually unnecessary. Your goal should be to deliver enough detail to avoid omissions problems and get complete the project.

3. **Eliminate a hierarchy of documents.** The conventional wisdom in the industry is that certain documents outweigh others. For instance, if there is a conflict between the specifications and the drawings, the specifications will supersede the drawings. The problem is that the courts don't embrace this hierarchy. Courts view both specifications and drawings as one unit, known simply as "contract documents." After all, if a conflict is found in a five-page document, one would not argue that page five supersedes the information on page three. So when a contractor brings a conflict to the owner, don't "wordsmith" the issue by pointing to a hierarchy of documents. This is also true with conflicts within drawing sets: large plans do not supersede small plans.

4. **Remember that drawings do not need to stand on their own merit.** If you have information about the civil site and show it on the electrical plan, that information is valid. However, there are some "multi-prime" states where work must be bid to multiple subcontractors for public work. This is an exception, as the right information must be on the right documents.

5. **Discourage general contractors from breaking up bid sets for distribution to subcontractors.** Similar to point three above, the holistic nature of the contract document applies here, and issues can arise when general contractors break up drawings and bid sets and give subs pieces of the package.

Competitive Bidding from the GC's Perspective

The insights and suggestions that follow have been culled from years of trial, error and lost opportunity. As general contractors, we are often are left shaking our heads wondering "If only they would understand...." While all of this may seem elementary to contractors, it may prove enlightening if you're responsible for contracting construction services.

Bid Period

A bid due-date of two weeks from the receipt of drawings is a good minimum standard for most jobs. Multi-million dollar projects should get three (possibly four) weeks.

Architects and clients who demand one week turnarounds are hurting themselves. In most cases, by the time drawings are received, analyzed, sorted reproduced, packaged and distributed to subcontractors at least a week has elapsed. Not allowing sufficient time to quote the project thoughtfully creates disinterest and may prompt dropouts. You also take the risk that general contractors and their subcontractors are "throwing" high prices at your project with the assumption that they will be "covered" if they get the job.

Give us enough time to quote your project; is one more week really going to make that much difference in the final analysis?

Bid Day

Generally speaking, Monday is not a good day. Do you remember that song? Bids might as well have been due the previous Friday. Despite assertions to the contrary, most of the contracting world and their subcontractors aren't slaving away on your job over the weekend.

Although some suppliers are open on weekends, contractors rarely can obtain quotes because estimating staffs are generally unavailable. Any day is better than Monday. As a rule, the later in the week the bids are due the better. When choosing a bid due-date, be aware of long weekends and holidays also. We get weak responses from our subcontractors during these times.

Bid Time

Deadlines between 2 p.m. and 5 p.m. are the best. A bid due-time of 9 a.m. or 10 a.m. doesn't make any sense: disrupting the sacred contractor coffee hour has never served anyone well. Allow us the benefit of most of the day to get organized.

Many architects and owners are surprised to learn that contractors don't have all their subcontractor and vendor prices until the last hour, and sometimes minutes, before deadline. Coffee breaks notwithstanding, there are at least three reasons this happens.

First, most subcontractors submit at the last minute. They are last in the information chain and some of their tardiness is unavoidable; they rely on prices from their vendors. Often these vendors may have only learned about your job the day bids are due. Lighting supply companies are notorious for last hour submittals, with no exceptions. Not one in the civilized world has ever been able to explain their reasons.

Secondly, the subcontractors of invited general contractors often respond to other general contractors on advertised jobs. Their loyalties lie with the general with whom they most often work, thus they bid late to everyone else. We will often get great unsolicited subcontractor bids at the very last minute – and we forgive their bad manners; including them can often make or break a bid.

Finally, addenda can create last-minute chaos, fear and loathing. Having forgiven the subs, now we must forgive the architects. We can't finalize our numbers until all the information from subcontractors and vendors arrives. When you consider all the factors involved, perhaps you can appreciate the difficulty we have pulling it all together.

Checklist for a Pre-Construction Meeting

A pre-construction meeting should be held at the site and include key project team representatives from the client, your firm, and the contractor. At every meeting, you need to address the following:

- ❑ Introductions
- ❑ Lines of communications and submittals, including correspondence
- ❑ Site rules and regulations
- ❑ Procedures for issuing and revising information and authorizing changes
- ❑ Survey information
- ❑ Contractor's designated areas and coordinating procedures
- ❑ Shop or erection drawing and submittal requirements
- ❑ Methods of payment
- ❑ Certificates of insurance
- ❑ Procedures for overtime and shift work
- ❑ Labor agreements (if applicable)

☐ Labor availability

☐ Security

☐ Clean up

☐ Safety and first aid

☐ Temporary facilities and services

☐ Project-schedule and Project-cost programs

☐ Material handling

☐ The Equal Employment Opportunity (EEO) Act

☐ Environmental procedures

☐ The client's role and responsibilities

☐ Specific state and local laws or regulations

☐ Procedures for claims and disputes

☐ Subcontractor approval

☐ Community relations

☐ Clarification of critical specifications

☐ Quality control

Construction Administration

Many owners require construction administration services by the design firm as a complement to an independent construction manager. These activities must necessarily precede the actual selection of (sub) contractors and include the following functions:

- Assist the client in determining contractor requirements for over-all warranty of labor, materials and equipment, and separate guarantee bonds for items that have warranty periods of more than one year.

- Assist the client in performing pre-bid walk-throughs.

- Assist the client in securing bids and tabulation and analysis of bid results, and furnish recommendations on the awarding of construction contracts.

- Provide consultation and advice to the client on the acceptance of subcontractors and other persons and organizations proposed by the prime contractor or contractors when such advice is required by the bidding documents.

- Provide consultation and advice to the client on the acceptance of substitute materials and equipment proposed by the contractor or contractors when substitution before the award of contracts is allowed by the bidding documents.

- Provide advice and consultation to the client during construction.

- Prepare the elementary and supplementary sketches that are required to resolve problems due to actual field conditions encountered.

- Check detailed construction drawings, shop or erection drawings, and erection drawings submitted by the contractor or contractors for compliance with design concepts.

- Review laboratory, shop, and mill test reports on materials and equipment.

18 Guidelines for A/E Site Observation

If you're an A/E project manager, refer to these guidelines as you set parameters for site etiquette. Your team members should know where their jurisdiction starts and ends before they set foot on the site.

1. Only one person from the designer's office should be designated as the authorized contract administrator to give directions or interpretations.

2. The principals of the firm are responsible for contract administration, regardless of whether a principal or an employee performs that service.

3. All design occurs before bidding. Once construction begins, design decisions are referred to as change orders.

4. Do not give the contractor the impression that you have more job site authority than you really do have. Be aware of your implied duties:

    - Don't interfere with the contractor's work.

    - Cooperate with the contractor.

    - Inform the contractor of information relevant to the job.

5. Assist the owner in coordinating any other contractors not under the general contractor's control.

6. When on-site, view the work for its conformance with the contract documents only. Document any discrepancies in writing.

7. Never tell or suggest the means or methods by which the contractor should accomplish the work.

8. Only give directions or interpretations to the general contractor, never to the subcontractor — unless the general contractor is present.

9. Do not interfere with the job site safety procedures of the contractor.

10. Establish a schedule of strategic site visits by project designers to aid the project representative.

11. Always provide project orientation sessions for project representatives with the design staff to properly familiarize them with the project details.

12. Establish communication procedures to route all correspondence between the A/E and the contractor through the project representative.

13. Coordinate all matters relating to interpretation of a consultant's work with the particular consultant involved.

14. Be especially observant of early construction because it's easier to correct mistakes early on.

15. Record all visits for site observation on standard forms.

16. Take and date photos and make notes on all site visits.

17. Don't be pressed into hasty decisions.

18. Keep the owner aware of construction progress and problems at all times.

Document Construction with a Daily Field Report

The Daily Field Report (DFR) gives your firm documented evidence of good performance. If done carelessly, it gives claimants documented evidence of bad performance.

Have your people in the field stick to the facts, and have them prepare their reports on the day the work is performed. A DFR should include:

- Date/Contract name and number
- Contractor's name
- Contractor's representative
- Weather
- Manpower and man-hours
- Major equipment used
- Description of work, location, progress, quantities installed related to work-hours, and/or specific bid items.
- Acceptability of work or description of deficiencies or non-conformance.
- Instructions to the contractor
- Compliance or noncompliance with directions given

- Visitors

- Accidents or major events

- Hours and equipment used

- Completion of milestones; if no work was done, list the reason(s)

Keep copies of these reports in a three ring binder in reverse chronological order, and use monthly tabs to divide the reports to facilitate retrieval. Have your field representative ask for a copy of the contractor's daily report and attach it to the DFR.

How to Present Construction Damages in a Dispute

The successful resolution of construction disputes is often directly related to how well the facts (and expert opinions) are perceived and received.

Whether you're negotiating a complex change order, making a presentation to an arbitrator or an alternative dispute resolution (ADR) panel, mediating a claim, or presenting testimony in court, the means and method of presentation is critical to the outcome.

Each forum requires a different presentation style in order to win over decision makers who may be skeptical of minutia involving convoluted time and financial damage issues that are time-consuming to present and digest.

While it's hoped that construction disputes don't end up in court, the wise project manager is always cognizant of the possibility, and being prepared for this eventuality is always smart.

What follows is an outline of procedures and possible structured formats that may be utilized during the presentation of time and cost damages.

Using these methods can provide the owner's (and contractor's) legal team with the advantage needed, at the most critical phase of any dispute resolution.

All construction damages are not created equal, nor should they be presented in a uniform format. The successful presentation of damages must first address the type of damages being claimed and, secondly, be prepared for a specific audience.

Construction dispute issues are primarily time and financial.

I. Time damages.

Time is money. However, the presentation of time damages may need vastly different presentation techniques than would be claimed for purely financial damages. *Typical time-related damages include:*

- Delay (total work stoppage or partial delays to critical work items),
- Productivity impacts,
- Constructive and directed acceleration.

a. **Fragnets**–A typical exhibit used to present time damages analysis and conclusions, as normally presented through expert testimony, is a time-scaled fragnet.

Fragnets are usually developed from an analysis of critical path method (CPM) schedules, daily reports, correspondence, and other records that provide a planned and as-built history of the work.

b. **Added time units**–The successful time extension claim will yield added time-units to the contract, which may make the contractor whole as it relates to the "time" element (interim milestone or final completion dates).

This often has dollar-related con-sequences, primarily when liquidated damages are a possibility.

c. **Typical mistakes**–Some typical mistakes made in the presentation of time damages are to make the exhibits too dense with information and too complex to be readily understood. The use of simple charts and tables, clearly understood by the decision maker, is necessary to demonstrate the analysis performed and the conclusions reached by the expert.

d. **Expert witnesses**–Expert witnesses should not use exhibits to show the complex minutia and detail of the analysis, but rather only a summary of opinions reached. A short, verbal presentation of the documents and steps taken to reach those opinions is all that is normally necessary.

The expert must be prepared to present the source documents and steps taken in the analysis. CPM schedule delay and impact analysis may lead to many interpretations, dependent upon the reliability and credibility of the source documents and analysis conducted.

II. Financial damages.

Financial damages are normally calculated as the difference between the as-contracted cost to do a definable element of work and the added cost to perform work as the result of a change, delay, or impact to that work.

The proper measure of financial damages is the identifiable increased cost beyond that contracted for a specific issue. It is not simply the total cost of doing the project minus the total contract price.

This is because total cost damages do not address partial or total responsibility of the different parties to the total actual cost of performance. The most common damage elements are as follows:

a. **Direct costs**—These are the costs of labor, equipment, materials, subcontractors and suppliers for definable items of work in a project. Direct costs are normally the easiest to document. They show the relationship between cause and effect.

b. **Productivity impacts**—Often the nature and impact of an event may cause labor and equipment productivity losses to the work separate from the direct additional cost of the event in question. The nature of productivity losses requires a significantly different approach to damage analysis and presentation than direct added costs of a change or delay.

c. **Job-site indirect costs**–These are costs for labor, equipment, and materials incurred on-site to support the direct work. Included are the supervision and project management costs necessary to support definable work elements. Capturing job-site overhead costs is normally a straightforward matter of reviewing the contractor's job cost reports, with the difficulty of tying an issue's direct costs to the associated job-site overhead costs.

d. **Home-office overhead costs**–These costs are incurred off-site and are the costs necessary to support both the job-site direct and indirect cost functions. The calculation is straightforward, but the formula can be controversial in its application and difficult to explain.

e. **Lost profit**–Lost profits usually are calculated based on a contractor's as-bid markup for anticipated profit as detailed in the cost estimate. In some instances a claim may be made for lost profits on other projects that were adversely impacted due to the events of the project in question. Lost profits on other jobs must be treated separately as they can be seen as speculative. It is much harder to demonstrate a direct link between events that caused a claim on the primary project in question and the costs claimed.

f. Other costs–These elements, not included above, include escalation costs, interest or cost of capital, liquidated and actual damages. All of these costs may be caused by changes and delays encountered during construction. Their presentation, when the facts are known, is usually straightforward.

g. Consequential business losses–These costs may include potential profits on future projects, lost bonding capacity, loss of business value, etc. Consequential business losses are normally very difficult to prove with "certainty" and require a totally different approach to analysis and presentation.

Financial and economic analysis experts, who analyze a contractor's overall financial condition using audited financial reports and other business documentation, can provide an estimate of the damages suffered.

III. Basic presentation methodology

Regardless of the damages being presented, the presentation should be keyed to the same style throughout. The case should present a uniform perspective of the facts and opinions so as not to surprise or confuse.

Brevity and simplicity both verbally and in the graphics used should be the underlying presentation principle, no matter what the audience's level of experience in construction contracts or time and cost issues. Often the most effective presentation is a summary of the analysis and opinions that demonstrates the credibility and validity of the facts and opinions expressed. In addition, follow these guidelines:

a. Simple, clean and clearly understood graphics and tables provide a focal point of discussion for the witness to educate the decision maker.

b. Time-scaled bar charts instead of complex flow diagrams and CPM logic charts provide a graphic that will hold the audience's attention as the presentation develops.

c. Overall site plans with the project's key features denoted can provide an understanding of the flow of the work and perspective of the work areas that cannot be made with words alone.

d. Still photos can provide details in support of facts but should not be overused, as they can be hard for non-technical audience members to decipher.

e. Videos are superior to still photos and are much easier to understand. They bring the entire project to life and provide minute details in a manner the viewer can more easily grasp than through still photos.

IV. Presentation forums

a. **Contractual, by change order**–During the construction phase of a project, the goal is to reach an early resolution of a change order or claim. Most often the parties settle the dispute, and the use of lawyers and consultants is unnecessary or limited.

The parties are intimately knowledgeable of the facts and are most knowledgeable of the technical issues. If a resolution is to occur, it will happen amicably as long as personalities or politics do not overreach the issue. Over 90 percent of all claims and disputes are settled in this tried-and-true manner.

Contracts typically detail procedures the parties are to follow when a change order is to be processed. Other provisions may apply when the parties reach an impasse in their negotiation of a change order.

The methodology to measure time and financial damages often differs within various contract provisions. These circumstances require a thorough understanding of which provision will govern.

The value of providing complete data in a simple format will always yield the best results.

In a typical contract change order, the use of established unit prices for specific elements of work may apply. Additionally, set markups for overhead, profit and bond costs may be delineated.

In some cases, such as a differing site condition (DSC), the contract may ignore the change order provisions and dictate the use of an equitable adjustment. In short, the parties are to negotiate a change order using whatever means agreeable to the parties for the direct and indirect costs for the DSC. This might be to follow the contract's change order provisions, or to use actual costs instead of stated unit prices and markups, since they may result in costs too high or too low for the issue or event.

b. **ADR arbitration**–Arbitrators, and alternative dispute resolution panel members, are normally individuals with professional experience in construction. Therefore, it is usually not necessary to educate the decisions makers. Occasionally highly technical facts may need to be overviewed. If the decision maker needs technical information, the outreach process is available based on their experience and most ADR formats.

Arbitrators and ADR panel members are most receptive to a clear, concise overview, with supporting detail entered into the record for review when the open session of the proceedings has been adjourned.

Assumption that material of value to the damages presentation is available to the decision makers is true only when formally placed in the record.

ADR, by its nature, is intended to be a more informal presentation process than that of a courtroom, but it is still a controlled environment. A supportive, non-confrontational approach yields results. Providing factual data, positive responses, and technically precise responses are all beneficial.

A clear picture of the damages and resolution sought is essential. The documentation must be complete and the analysis clear, as this is what the professionals on the panel expect from all parties.

c. **Civil/private contracts litigation**–When a claim issue reaches the courtroom, it is, by its very nature, one that is complicated by the process of not having reached resolution at any of the early settlement stages associated with contract construction.

The tendency is to continue in the same vein as used by the parties when dealing with their knowledgeable counterparts during the change order process or review. Using these types of presentations is not likely to yield a favorable jury decision.

The legal team must educate and sway a jury to the value of the claim. Simple presentations using non-technical language and clear graphics is key.

Photographs and videos will familiarize the court and jury with the project and the claim. The context must be established, followed by the details necessary to fully represent the damages.

The owner and/or the claimant should select the trial attorney on the presentation methodology the attorney uses, with consideration of the type of claim being tried.

Not only are there attorneys who specialize in construction claims presentation, but there are those who have specialties within construction litigation. The right legal team for the job is crucial.

d. **Government contracts litigation**–Government litigation, especially at the federal level, is a specialized type of contract litigation.

Whether presentation before a Board or before a federal court is anticipated, an attorney with experience in this arena is essential. You are hiring your presentation. It is expensive and needs to represent your position, both by style and by experience.

V. Conclusions

Contract claims result from a failure by the owner and the contractor to reach equitable adjustments to their contract. Most are solved by the change order process. Less than 10 percent must resort to more complicated forms of ADR or to litigation.

Whatever the process used, many of the rules for a successful presentation are the same:

a. The forum and type of damages being presented will dictate the best strategy of presentation. In all cases it is imperative to keep graphics and explanations and presentation clear and concise.

b. Use plans, maps, still photos and videos to familiarize and not to overwhelm. Use detailed materials to illustrate, not to complicate.

c. The' expert must have a concise presentation, leaving detail for cross-examination.

d. Key witnesses should be skilled in presentations, and expert in the particular environment in which the claim is to be heard. The owner and/or the contractor should select the legal team, presenter, and/or litigator to fit both the claim and the claimants.

The Advantages of a Project Policy

Project policies offer an attractive option to risk managers and owners looking for iron-clad professional liability coverage for their construction projects.

Traditionally, owners have relied on design firms to have their own practice policies to provides PL protection. This presents an administrative headache as multiple certificates of insurance must be gathered and tracked.

Plus, should a claim arise, there's no guarantee that coverage will be there when needed. The design firm may have dropped coverage, or policy limits may have been exhausted by previous claims.

Look for these advantages in a project policy:

- **One project, one policy**. All members of the design team can be covered under a single policy, easing administration.

- **Owner-controlled terms**. The owner chooses the policy limits and the duration of coverage – often available up to ten years after project completion. No more worrying whether design team members have enough insurance.

- **Guaranteed coverage**. Project policies are typically noncancelable, as long as the premiums are paid and no material misrepresentations have been made.

- **Set premium**. The premium rate won't rise for the life of the policy, so there are no budget surprises.

- **Dedicated limits**. The policy limits cover your project – and your project only. No chance of limits being exhausted by other claims.

- **Single-point claims responsibility**. There's no finger pointing about who's to blame and which professional liability insurance company is responsible.

- **Added features**. Some insurers offer value-added services to their project policies. With DPIC TeamCover Project Insurance, for example, DPIC Companies will share the cost of a formal "partnering" program to promote a commitment to common goals and effective problem solving among all project participants.

Who Pays?

Typically the owners, since they hold the policy. However, costs can be shared with design firms through premium reimbursements or negotiated lower fees. (Since fees on the project won't be counted to determine the firms' practice policy premiums, they save money when working on projects covered by project policies.)

Accepting   Substitutions   for   Specified Materials

Much has been written, mostly negative, regarding "or equal" substitutions. On one hand, you do not want to discourage innovation or eliminate competition. On the other hand, you do not want a job impacted or your own costs significantly increased processing inappropriate or numerous substitution requests. How can your costs and exposures to claims be minimized?

- Recognize that, in the real world, substitution requests are inevitable. Therefore, develop proprietary specifications that clearly define performance characteristics and other requirements without drafting an illusory, tailor-made specification that only allows one manufacturer to comply.

- Include as part of the specification a "Substitute Request Form" that must accompany any proposed "or equal" substitution. This form should fully set forth the criteria that will be used in reviewing acceptance of a substitution.

- Enforce the specifications or general condition requirements pertaining to substitutions, as well as all other provisions. You may either directly waive any substitution provision by not enforcing it, or may indirectly waive it by not enforcing other contractual requirements.

- Be responsive to requests received. Courts and arbitrators do not look kindly upon responses or rejections that do not address the issue in a timely or professional manner.

Don't Get Tripped Up by Claims

"Claim" is one of the dirty words of our industry. Why? Because every E & O claim made against your firm puts your reputation and business on the line. Handle it improperly and a claim can wreck your corporate image, ruin existing and future proposals, and lead to disastrous outcomes in court. Here are some guidelines:

There are several steps in processing a claim, and proper documentation is essential. Each formally presented claim should be sequentially numbered and a copy promptly sent to the project manager and to the client.

A letter is sent to the contractor acknowledging receipt of the claim. Ignoring a claim until the end of a job will hamper the possibility of an early and successful settlement of the claim.

Set a "reasonable time" in which to respond to the claim, and advise the contractor of this time frame in the letter of receipt. Some claims are sufficiently complex that a 60- or 90-day response time is reasonable. A 30-day response time is adequate for simple claims.

Immediate denial of a claim may trigger an arbitration demand or set off the litigation process. Once this occurs, quick settlement is almost impossible.

An analysis of the claim should be given a high priority:

- All facts checked for accuracy

- Records kept for negotiation/ settlement purposes

- All project records reviewed to make a complete file on the claim event.

Field records, schedule submittals, payment applications, meeting minutes, photographs, and telephone conversation memoranda should all be researched for anything related to the claim and filed for efficient retrieval.

The contractor must prove the case and submit all documentation and data concerning the alleged claim. If gaps or holes appear in the contractor's submittals, ask for substantiating records of the contractor's responses.

The reviewer should handle the merits of a claim separately from any analysis of entitlement to time or money.

A proper and objective analysis of a claim should consider all viewpoints and identify:

- What actually happened

- When it happened

- Who was responsible

- How the contract documents should be applied to the claim situation.

When the engineer, the contractor, and the reviewer are satisfied with the analysis and recommendations, they should discuss the proposed settlement. If negotiations are necessary, keep a record of all agreements, disagreements, and compromises. Include the supporting rationale.

If an agreement can be reached within the recommended limits, the client approves the commitment. After approvals, a change order will be issued to permit payment to the contractor. A change order records the final resolution of a claim.

If an impasse does occur, the claims analysis, recommendation, and all supporting data and documents are submitted to the client for review.

After legal review, the claim may be rejected with explanation, or additional information may be requested and negotiation recommended.

If there are still outstanding claims after the final acceptance, they can be excluded from the Final Release Certificate and Indemnity.

Causes of Claims

In order to avoid claims, all parties to the contract need to understand fully the causes of claims. The following outlines 10 causes of contract claims:

1. **Delayed completion.** A late project can have major cost impacts on both the contractor and the client. Determination and proof of liability can be difficult. All parties to the contract must take

scheduling very seriously and maintain proper job records to support or refute this type of claim.

2. **Changed time frame**. Any change in starting or ending dates should be reviewed carefully for cost and schedule impacts.

3. **Restricted work sequence**. Any sequence of work restriction as a result of existing operations or the work of a separate contractor must be clearly stated in the contract documents.

4. **Chain of command**. Every project has an organizational structure (i.e., supplier reports to sub, sub reports to G.C., etc.) that must not be violated. Prepare an organizational chart at the start of the project, and make sure all parties follow it.

5. **Failure to coordinate**. The client of a multi-prime contract project and the general contractor with several subs have certain duties to coordinate the work. Failure to provide this coordination may result in cost increases and claims.

6. **Quantity variations**. Substantial changes in the quantity of work to be accomplished (plus or minus) can greatly affect the unit cost of the work. This possibility should be addressed in the contract with a quantity-variation clause.

7. **Quality of work**. Very difficult to define in words. Too often the engineer is left to determine proper quality, and often this results in disputes. When possible, make reference to some existing work or written standard, rather than resorting to the use

of terms such as "workmanlike," "reasonable," and "standard for the industry."

8. **Access to work area.** Any restriction on access to the work area by one party to another party should be clearly explained in the contract documents.

9. **Failure of project to function properly.** If the contractor is to be responsible for the performance of the project (i.e., watertight walls, rates of production, etc.), then the contractor also must design the work. The contractor cannot be given a detailed set of drawings and specs, be required not to deviate, and then guarantee the results of the engineer's design.

10. **Ambiguous contract documents.** Any contract containing words and phrases that are not clear (i.e., "reasonable," "timely," "workmanlike," "reasonably workmanlike," etc.) will be subject to interpretation and claims. Final interpretation will usually be by a judge or an arbitrator.

Before bidding on the construction, the plans should be thoroughly reviewed for discrepancies that could result in claims.

Criteria for Claims

Before bidding construction, the plans should be reviewed for discrepancies that could result in claims. Nevertheless, even though a project may be well defined, the contract thorough and well-thought-out, and all parties in synch, legitimate claims can still arise.

When considering a formal claim under a contract, the following criteria apply:

- The claim arises after the contract execution by the contractor and client.

- The event could not be anticipated by reasonable parties.

- The unexpected event affects project costs, project schedule, planned means and methods, procedures, and/or performance of the work.

- The event adversely affects one of the parties to the contract.

- The claim is presented as a written request for additional time or money under the provisions of the contract documents.

All elements of a claim event must be present when a formal claim is filed. The total burden of proof regarding a claim falls on the party making the claim. This rule concerning construction claims prevails regardless of whether the claim is filed by the contractor against the client or vice versa.

Submittal Format

A claim submittal format should be established and agreed to with the contractor during the early stages of the project. All claims are to be documented and checked for validity under the terms of the contract:

- Did the contractor comply with the specific "notice of claim" requirements in the contract?

- Does the claim sufficiently justify additional money or time?

- Is the amount of money or time demanded proven by the data submitted, and is this amount reasonable compared to an independent estimate?

Claims Analysis

Claims and changes are among the most discussed and often misunderstood areas of construction contracts. One of the principal challenges of construction administration is to provide a system for handling these two important subjects. Claims and changes are an integral part of the construction process, and good claims administration principles are as important as good engineering, safety, cost, and scheduling.

Claims and changes should be viewed as processes required to handle construction events that take place where the contract leaves off: changed conditions, design changes, defective specifications, delays, disruptions, and accelerations.

Claims are unresolved disputes involving requests by the contractor for additional compensation and/or time that appear to be outside the scope of the contract. Unfortunately, the position is often taken that all claims are a nuisance, lack merit, border on the fraudulent, and result from the incompetence and/or stubbornness of the contractor.

Submitted claims could lead to lengthy disputes, polarized personalities, bitter arguments, and frequent and unpleasant association with a variety of lawyers – all culminating in settlements that the contractor feels are inadequate, the engineer considers exorbitant, and the client believes to be the fault of the engineer.

Types of Claims

The most common claims are those associated with the following situations or conditions:

Acceleration

Ambiguity

Bankruptcy

Bidding errors

Breach of contract

Cardinal changes

Changed conditions

Changes in quality or detail

Changes in dimension

Codes and conflicts

Constructive changes

Failure to provide access

Fast track projects

Hold harmless clauses

Impossibility/impracticality

Improper retainage

Improper rejection

Interference

Deceleration

Defective specifications

Delay

Differing site conditions

Disruption

Errors and omissions

Excessive inspection

Excessive management

Excessive testing

Failure to coordinate

Failure to perform

Nonpayment

Over-inspection

Owner conflict Refusal of change order

Substantial completion

Substitution problems

Subsurface conditions

Latent conditions	Supervision by others
Liquidation damages	Trade practices
Misinterpretation	Warranty provisions
Misrepresentation Negligence	Weather

The first step in dealing with claims is to recognize them early and to begin to document properly all related circumstances. Second, determine whether a valid basis exists for the claim. Third, assess how much the claim is worth based upon the accumulated documentation. Fourth, maintain a positive attitude, and make every effort to negotiate a prompt, equitable settlement according to the terms of the contract.

This information was provided by John Cornish.

Prescription for Avoiding Construction Claims

Here's the top ten ways to avoid claims during construction, according to an expert in the construction industry.

1. **Project delivery system**–Realize that there are various contracting relationships which will govern your rights as well as your obligations.

2. **Risk allocation**–Decide upon what risks you will assume or shift. Only then can the contract documents reflect requirements accurately.

3. **Contract**–Ensure that the contract documents reflect requirements accurately.

4. **Partnering**–Initiate a program to establish a relationship throughout the construction process to maintain open communication and trust. The true test of commitment is when a disagreement occurs.

5. **Change order management**–Changes in construction are inevitable—there is no such thing as a project without changes. The key is to provide for full and final settlement of all time and cost issues in a timely manner.

6. **Facts**–Document, on a daily basis, what is happening; do not rely on the memories of site personnel; as someone once said, "Memories fade, but paper only turns yellow."

7. **People**–Know the strengths and weaknesses of your personnel to avoid placing them in roles in which they cannot adequately perform. Remember, their failures and shortcomings become yours.

8. **Time and cost considerations**–Increased cost resulting from delay and disruption are typically the "big ticket" items when it comes to construction claims. Analysis to determine who or what caused the delay or disruption, and the resulting dollar damages, is critical and can be effectively performed if you have a reliable record of the facts.

9. **Coordination of responsibilities**–Know who has the contract responsibility to coordinate the work and whether actual performance reflects that. This area has great potential for creating disputes

and, of course, for affecting the project completion date.

10. **Schedule impacts**–In construction, time is definitely money. Force the issue to resolve schedule impacts as soon as they occur—i.e., determine if time extensions are required. At best, resolve them; at worst, develop a comprehensive, current record for subsequent resolution.

Combating Claims from RFIs

Here's how to handle the issue of contractors who submit high numbers of Request For Information (RFIs) in order to create extra change orders. The following samples outline the tactics they use.

1. Include clearly identifiable ambiguities in the contract documents which should have been addressed in the pre-bid process.

2. Submit a significant number of RFIs with the purpose of establishing a paper trail to support their subsequent claim for damages related to a faulty design or poor construction documents.

3. Overwhelm the designer with RFI's in the hope that the firm fails to timely respond and thus establish a claim for delay damages.

4. Attempt to obtain approval for alternative construction methods or substitute items which are less costly than those specified.

5. Perform the work identified in the response to the RFI and then belatedly seeking a change order after the work is done.

Take Precautions

Your best safeguard against these types of RFIs is through making sure you have provisions for responding to an RFI, and educating your firm on the RFI and claims process. Create a written protocol that sets forth requirements for RFI submittals, which should include:

1. What will and will not be accepted in an RFI

2. A statement that information which is discernable from the contract documents will not be addressed in an RFI response.

3. Documentation required for the RFI, including supporting data.

4. The time frame for responding to RFIs.

5. Clarification that the design professional response is not a change order or directive authorizing an increase in construction cost or time.

6. Any response from you will not address construction means or methods, or construction site safety issues.

7. The use of the RFI process is limited to a clarification of the contract documents and the designer will not review requests for substitute items as an RFI. Firms should review the RFI

protocol at the outset of each project and provide the contractor with the protocol at the preconstruction meeting.

Handle Daily Field Reports with Care

The Daily Field Report (DFR) gives your firm documented evidence of good performance. If done carelessly, it gives claimants documented evidence of bad performance.

In preparing a DFR, stick to the facts; this is no place for opinions. Prepare it on the day the work is performed and include:

- Date/Contract name and number
- Contractor's name
- Contractor's representative
- Weather
- Manpower and man-hours
- Major equipment used
- Description of work, location, progress, quantities installed related to work-hours, and/or specific bid items.
- Acceptability of work or description of deficiencies or non-conformance.
- Instructions to the contractor
- Compliance or noncompliance with directions given

- Visitors

- Accidents or major events

- Hours and equipment used

- Completion of milestones or if no work was done, the reasons

The report is prepared and numbered consecutively for each contract day, whether or not work is done. Gaps when no work occurred may be covered on a single report noting duration and reasons for the delay.

Keep DFRs in a three-ring binder in reverse chronological order. Use monthly tabs to divide the reports to facilitate retrieval.

The design firm should ask for a copy of the contractor's daily report and attach it to the DFR. A copy of both reports should go to the PM each week. If required by contract, the client should receive a copy also.

Using Photography for Field Engineering

The following activities are normally provided at the jobsite by the design firm and are referred to as Field Engineering during the construction phase.

To facilitate these activities, a digital camera should be obtained at the beginning of each construction effort to record and document the progress. A routine should be established for picture taking that will specify how often photos are to be taken and who will be responsible for taking them.

Some typical activities:

- Periodic visits to the project site at intervals appropriate to the various stages of construction to observe the progress and the quality of the executed work and report back to the client.

- Special inspections and testing of the work, and decisions as to the acceptance of the work.

- Determining the amount of progress payments due, based on the recorded completion of work, and recommending issuance of such payments by the client.

- Observing and recording initial operation of the project or of any performance tests required by the specifications.

- Making a final inspection and reporting on completion of the project, including recommendations regarding final payments to contractors and release of retained percentages, if any.

Photographs should be taken periodically to show construction progress. Also, they can document a particular problem that delays, disrupts, or interferes with the progress of the field operation.

When it comes to documenting what happened on a project, the best advice is to "take a lot of pictures." Construction photos can show what work was done and when, its quality (or lack of), differing site conditions (or lack of), and countless other pertinent facts.

At a minimum, one full roll of color film should be shot each week for each project.

Be sure to take photographs...

> When opening or changing traffic routing
>
> When placing protective barricades
>
> Of disputed work
>
> Of work that has to be duplicated, replaced, or removed
>
> Of completed false work
>
> Of extra work
>
> Of changed conditions

Identify each photograph: Put a unique serial number on the face of each photo, then provide a separate index listing the following information:

- Date, time, location, street name, centerline station, area, unit

- View—looking in which direction

- Description of activity, area, person

- Taken by (photographer)

It is advisable to purchase a good quality 35mm camera that is equipped with a data back—or a mega-pixel digital camera. Wide-angle lenses should not be used because they don't show enough detail. Use an item (ruler or hand) in close-up photos to establish scale. File the negatives in a different location from the prints.

Documenting the Project with Photography

When performing construction administration for a client, make sure to obtain a camera at the beginning of the construction effort. Photographs should be taken periodically to show construction progress. Also, they can document a particular problem which delays, disrupts, or interferes with the progress of the field operation.

When it comes to documenting what happened on a project, the best advice is to "take a lot of pictures." Construction photos can show what work was done and when, quality (or lack of), differing site conditions (or lack of), and countless other pertinent facts. At the beginning of each project, a routine should be established for picture taking that will specify how often photos are to be taken and who will be responsible for taking them. Be sure to take photos...

> When opening or changing traffic routing.
>
> When placing protective barricades.
>
> Of disputed work.
>
> Of work that has to be duplicated, replaced, or removed.
>
> Of completed false work.
>
> Of extra work.
>
> Of changed conditions.

Identify each photograph on the face with a unique serial number, and provide a separate index showing specific information.

Computer Cams for Construction Administration

Not every worker is happy to have a camera trained on the jobsite and the images shared on a project Internet site. But most employees see it as a benefit for everyone— for these reasons:

- Meeting minutes are posted promptly, and action items get a faster response.

- The hazards of "every-week-or-so" jobsite visits are reduced.

- Site problems really do get solved.

When an RFI (Request for Information) is posted for the entire team to see, there's a psychological incentive not to let the issue go unaddressed. Everyone sees there's an unresolved issue, and there's a little more pressure to act on it.

What normally takes several days of faxes and phone calls gets resolved in an afternoon. The truth is that project extranets really work.

In addition, jobsite video cameras have a public relations value, and corporations and public agencies are right on top of it.

Web Site Technology for Project Management

Within two years, more than 75 percent of all projects will be managed over the web.

Want to give your clients who are off-site instant access to daily activities on their projects? Combine today's full range of software and digital technology in a project-specific web site (or Extranet), and you can do just that.

Extranets enable information sharing and project management from a remote location. An Extranet can be hosted either in-house, using off-the-shelf software, or through an application service provider (ASP). An Extranet becomes a system of streamlining communication and maximizing information.

Getting started

It's important to review all the features of your Extranet with the entire project team. You must establish protocols and determine who will be responsible for each activity. It's good to start small and build; as you become familiar with the "feature-rich" technology, add more activities.

Advantages to the Client

For the client, the major advantage of an Extranet is instant access by the project team. A local presence is unnecessary; the client can have the best people on the project regardless of location. The client can also get updates without visiting the site.

Advantages to the Design Firm

For the design firm, the Extranet increases the speed of communication during design phases. Quick sketches can be posted to the site with little effort. This produces faster buy-in by the client, who now has more control and a speedier way to respond.

Decisions about structural remediation or color coordination of samples can be made quickly and inclusively by using photos from a digital camera.

Some web site software has built-in forms, such as field reports and notifications. At the end of a project, electronic archiving puts all these pieces together.

Advantages to the Construction Manager

An Extranet can be most helpful to the construction manager during the early part of the building process. All conversations with city officials, approvals, and the like can be recorded and posted. Later, photo updates are possible without actual site visits.

Other uses include RFI's on unforeseen site conditions, submittals, meeting notes, and correspondence. Have you considered that for a conference call with as many as 30 people and a dozen pages of meeting notes, information can be downloaded to all participants in less than an hour?

The Challenges

Many first-time project web site users may have to change their methods and even their thinking. Instead of approaching an Extra- net as a shared file cabinet, it should be viewed more like a live bulletin board.

The "tone" of email messages posted becomes important, and users have to establish a comfort level with the security, as both contractors and subcontractors are in the loop.

Limitations

Take note: an Extranet isn't as useful for jobs of short duration. Another drawback is that real-time communication is not guaranteed. And like the telephone, an Extra- net can be a little impersonal. You are not dealing face-to-face, and if the job is well done, there's nothing in the world like "being there."

The Benefit of Project Websites

If your firm is still holding out on using project-specific Websites or extranets, your competition may have a step up on you. What's the value of this tool? There are many:

- A password accessed, project Website provides your clients access to daily activities on their projects.

- It speeds project delivery by enabling information sharing and project management from remote locations at any time of the day or night.

- It streamlines communication while maximizing information to all parties.

- Because a local presence is not necessary, this method allows your clients to have the best people on the project, regardless of location.

- Design phase communication is accelerated, through posting of sketches to the site.

- Decision-making is accelerated on structural remediation, color coordination, and other issues that require visual review.

- Paperwork can be expedited with online field reports, notifications, and other forms.

Project websites provide high value to clients, and have numerous associated costs. Some of those costs you may decide to bill as mark-up reimbursables, or you may decide to include this service in your overall fee. In either case, you should calculate just what the service will cost, and estimate just value it provides, so that you can price appropriately.

Risks Come with Rewards When Using Project Websites

While project websites may enhance communications and data sharing, there are concerns. Consider the following issues:

- **Inadvertent increase in project responsibilities.** There is the danger that you could be held responsible for all content on the website. Other participants could also hold you liable for any copyright violations, harassment or other wrongful acts that occur in this virtual space.

- **Project delays.** While a primary motive for managing a project extranet is enhanced and improved communication, it may just as easily become the reason communication breaks down, say in the event of a network failure.

- **Project safety issues.** There is the possibility that design members may be tempted to suggest construction means and methods on the website and unintentionally become a participant in safety issues.

- **Ownership and use issues.** Will suppliers and detailers be able to readily use your documents? Are you then liable for their errors in dimensions and details?

- **Security.** Unauthorized access to your data or your client's can compromise your business or your project. This risk is not just from those firms that are authorized to access the project website. Hackers, the cat burglars and vandals of the Internet, can do an enormous amount of damage by changing data, stealing valuable information or wreaking havoc with a network.

- **Copyright or license infringement.** Illegal downloading of licensed software or copyrighted documents via the website can leave participants facing lawsuits.

- **Inadequate compensation**. Unless your contract provides for it, you may not be adequately compensated for the additional time required to train for, set up and coordinate the website effort.

What Can an Extranet Do for You?

For the A/E industry, the potential benefits of Internet technology are enormous. Now is the time to use project extranets to gather your partners from scattered locations into "cyber teams." Making this move will help you save time, cut costs, and boost productivity. It will get you collaborating in ways we haven't yet thought of.

With the Internet's potential to bring together A/E/C players into virtual "meeting rooms" and thus to speed and improve project delivery, and with the burgeoning number of extranet (project-specific) web sites clamoring for clients, it would seem that now is the time for any A/E firm to go fully online and ramp up into knowledge-based production.

Extranets boast many features:

- Password protection
- Platform or browser independence
- E-mail notification
- File tracking and viewing

- CADD document review and redlining features

- User-friendly interface, with good technical support

A Few of the Overall Benefits

- Time and money savings (because all the information is stored in a centralized location)

- Easy storage of photographs online (so issues can be settled with- out the parties having to travel)

- Simple data archiving to CD in the same format as the Web page (for quick reference in the future)

Equipment Required

It's important to have the same equipment in the office and on the job site. This includes:

- Computer with high-speed Internet access

- Internet Service Provider (ISP) for email delivery

- Digital camera

What can an extranet really do for you? An extranet can serve your firm in three principal ways:

1. Speed document access and distribution.

An extranet acts as a central clearinghouse for all project-related documents, simultaneously serving all team members whether they are in Philadelphia or the Philippines. Just by clicking, you can view and redline memos, meeting notes, drawings, sketches, schedules, specifications, field reports, and more.

So, rather than waiting for "snail mail" or FedEx, you can have instantaneous posting of and access to exactly the document you need at the moment you need it.

Thus, no one on the team need wait for commercial printing and delivery of new drawings whenever a change is ordered. Instead, notes Bob Tedeschi of the New York Times News Service, "...the most up-to-date blueprints can be posted on the site, with email notifications going out to anyone who needs to know. Work schedules can also be emailed or posted to a particular page on the site, so that different teams can track how the job is proceeding."

In other words, an extranet links you to everyone else on the project. By helping team members to focus on the most critical tasks—rather than on paperwork—it can boost efficiency, improve project workflow, and reduce time to market.

2. Streamline organization and workflow.

An extranet creates for each document an audit trail that shows everyone who posted, revised, viewed, downloaded, or redlined it—with the dates of all those transactions. It thus illuminates roles and provides a clear record of events.

All communications are archived in a form that cannot be edited. Just think of the lawsuits that could be avoided by the mere existence of an indisputable record of all project communications."

The system also strengthens accountability. If an RFI elicits no response by an agreed-upon time, it is flagged, and the recipient and/or the PM receives an email.

3. Promote real-time collaboration.

According to current research from the CAD for Principals Council, a key requirement for future A/E/C electronic processing is that "We no longer draw; we create a digital model. We must collaborate on the model, not on drawings. This collaboration must include team members from outside organizations."

For architects and engineers, this means the long-range goal for extranets is for design team players in all locations to "meet" and work together on models, solve problems, and agree on changes—all without having to leave their offices.

By fluidly interacting with other project principals in the conceptual design mode, they will be able to apply creative thinking throughout and see their best concepts become reality.

Although the realization of this dream is down the line, it will mean that with an extranet, you will ultimately base your team's modus operandi on a 3D model whence all changes begin. The user will be able to extract dimensions and quantities from the model—or update the model by changing a dimension.

In other words, a good extranet source will enable a top-down approach to project management. It will allow you to think like an architect, not a draftsperson.

While we wait for this reality, an extranet site can still help you collaborate. Your team members can conduct a dialogue by posting questions and answers on the site. They can set up online design reviews, hold threaded discussions, and email each other from within the site. They can interactively redline and comment on drawings without necessarily being a CAD user. And by doing so online, they save measurable costs and inconvenience.

Boost Your Branch Office Performance with an Extranet

An extranet can bring special value to branches collaborating on a project. Also termed a project-specific web site, an extranet allows "three-dimensional," real-time sharing of project knowledge between the contracting office and branch offices, customers, suppliers, and vendors around the country and the world.

An extranet can help you bring together your business partners into a high-gear, knowledge-based operation. And it can do so for reasonable fees.

With an extranet, all team members, no matter where their location, get instant, 24-hour access to shared files, such as meeting notes, correspondence, project schedules, bulletins, specifications, budgets, drawings, construction documents, RFIs, submittal databases, and site photos.

Big-decision response time drops, clients can review designs on-line, and fewer site meetings are needed, saving everyone time and money. The project manager can store and track all project information in one location. Through electronics, the "branch" becomes part of the "trunk."

An Extranet Scenario

Consider these specific benefits of the extranet to this hypothetical work in progress.

A multi-million-dollar, multi-faceted project has an extended project team of over 20 firms and branches scattered across the country. Because of the project's scope, frenetic pace, and fast-track schedule, project management has elected to set up a collaborative project web site.

Any project team member (with security clearance) can log on to the site and actually create, edit, delete, or rename project files, which are indexed and fully searchable.

A threaded discussion link for the project enables team members to talk with each other in real-time. Using a CAD program, members can share designs among 2 or 200 users at the same time. Each user can actually drive the application or interact directly from his or her remote location.

When construction begins, information becomes available to field crews. The resident engineers have Web access, and they can instantaneously forward their questions to whoever has the answers—the client, the home office, or the local branch. Rather than a four-day turnaround for an RFI, they can hear back within a day.

Extranets are for Everyone

Project-specific web sites involve a balance of internal and external information. Since they use standard Web technology, even the most technologically challenged people on the project team can participate and collaborate.

Standard Web browsers provide point-and-click interface, global access, and complete independence from proprietary hardware and software.

Plus, they require only nominal entry fees. A typical plan might range from $300 per month for 40 users and 40 megabytes of storage to $1,500 per month for 500 users and 500 megabytes of storage.

Collaboration Using IT Brings Speed, Quality, and Results

Information technology enables collaboration on a level never before possible in this industry. With an extranet, multiple handling among business partners goes away.

In a request for material change, for example, all parties, from supplier to owner, can deal with the request concurrently, reach agreement, compress schedules, and roll the project along. Everyone is on the same page.

Consider a school that plans to open a new building in August—but the required brick is temporarily unavailable. The school board decides to use "faux" brick, which they can obtain more readily and inexpensively.

In a traditional scenario, this change process could command both time and excessive mental energy. The material supplier would consider the change and pass his information to the contractor, who would contact the designer, who would then talk with the owner.

But put the request for change on the Extranet, notify everyone by email, and all players can be "online" with the information inside the hour.

Beyond material changes, you also can plug in meeting notes, drawings, specifications, schedules, even budgets. The principle is the same. Once all the players are lined up, you can have your project steaming along, folks from different functional organizations reading the same real-time updates and talking with one another—by phone or chat—as though they were all traveling by train, discussing the same view.

CHAPTER 12

WRAPPING UP THE PROJECT

Closeout in a Nutshell

If we had to sum up the most critical aspects of project closeout in one article, it would look something like this:

1. **The key to success is to use checklists—lots of checklists.** If you have read this column over the years, then you already understand this. When planning the other phases of the project, there is usually some logical sequence to completing the tasks. Most of this disappears during the final 10 percent. Your focus should now shift to crossing off items on various checklists until none remain.

2. **Don't allow anyone to work on any item that is not on the checklist.** This is extremely important. People will always find something more interesting to do than close out punch-list items. These distractions waste the budget and do nothing to complete the project. Insist on frequent meetings, sometimes several times a day, to keep the focus on closeout.

3. **Build your firm's intellectual capital through "lessons learned."** At the end of each project, collect the lessons learned by the project team and work them into improving the firm's processes. Perform the project completion analysis and document what went well and what did not. Be a learning organization—don't repeat past mistakes.

4. **Make every effort to safeguard the project records.** If trying to find the back-up calculation for a certain structure is difficult when the project is in the design phase, it's impossible five years later! Leaving all your project records in file cabinets until someone else needs the cabinets is not records management.

5. **Don't forget to ask for a referral from your client.** Make sure this is a routine event at the closeout of every project. Get the referral on the client's official letterhead, signed by the most senior manager possible. Remember, you can always say you did something, but having it in writing from your client is proof you did.

6. **Plan your project completion party at the start of the project.** Successful project teams start by planning for success, and then they execute the plan. If the project schedule indicates the completion party as a separate milestone, the team is looking forward to success. Make sure you allocate budget to make it happen.

Success Steps During Closeout

The project closeout phase is a distinct phase requiring its own management, and you must assure that all administrative aspects of finalizing the contract are met.

Project closeout should always include these critical steps:

- **Identify final tasks that require completion.** Develop a project completion plan with critical activities.

- **Reassign staff as required.** Labor costs are the most significant controllable cost of a project. Early de-staffing and reassignment of non-essential team members will improve the financial success of the project.

- **Release equipment and materials for use on other projects.** Assess leases and other agreements for project equipment and materials for a timely breakdown and disbanding of the project office.

- **Finalize accounting and close books.** Plan for the required procurement and accounting actions to closeout vendor purchase accounts. Establish a plan to discontinue project services such as utilities and mail.

- **Final meeting and report.** Arrange with the client for a final project meeting to clarify and finalize all project tasks and submit all project records.

Once you've completed project close-out activities, send a final written notice of completion to the client or owner.

Even after the client has acknowledged the notice, however, you may need to continue working on project-related matters. If so, be sure to establish a central contact person to communicate with the client about how requests will be handled and billed.

Make clear to the client your availability for post-project tasks. you don't want a team member providing continued and non-reimbursed support to the client six months after the final invoice has been submitted and the project books are closed!

Seven Keys to Successful Project Photography

A photograph is worth a thousand words, so the saying goes. And for your project, professional photography can provide numerous benefits in marketing the project and also in helping your company market its services in the future.

Professional photographs should be taken at milestones in the project's development—when dramatic events take place—and certainly at the project's completion. A budget for professional photography should be included in your project budget.

1. **Find a good photographer:**
   - Check directory listings for professional societies and organizations, such as SMPS (Society for Marketing Professional Services), and AIA.
   - Ask your colleagues.

- Look at brochures of competitors or colleagues in the industry, and check the photo credits in the ones you like.

2. Once you have contacted a photographer:

- Ask to see work samples.

- Select someone you're comfortable with.

- Make sure the candidate is accustomed to photographing construction as well as the finished project.

3. Decide whether you want 35 mm slides, negatives from which you can make prints, digital files, or 4 x 5 inch transparencies. Transparencies work well for the completed project, particularly if you plan to enlarge the photo or submit it for publication.

4. Make sure you determine usage rights for the photos— one time or unlimited. As you will undoubtedly want to use the photograph in future marketing efforts, you may want to negotiate unlimited use.

5. Be sure to give the photographer specific directions:

- Try to accompany the photographer on the shoot. If you can't, then provide specific directions.

- Determine whether or not you are going to need an aerial photo, close-ups of project details, or an overall portrait photo.

6. Since photos should be taken at milestones in the project, particularly at dramatic moments of construction,

create a plan at the project's inception that notes when photography should take place.

- Try to shoot in good weather so you will have a bright blue sky in your photo.

7. Once you have your photos:

- Send out a press release to trade publications and to your local newspapers at milestones in the project's development, and include a captioned photo. Remember, you'll have greater success in getting coverage with a good photo.

- Always check with clients on any publicity you send out, and be sure you have client approval.

- When the project is finished, frame a portrait of the project for your client.

- Use the photo on a post card announcing the project completion and its unique features.

- Plan to use project photos for future award entries, brochures or other marketing materials you develop. Your investment will pay off with a permanent record in your files that can be used again and again.

Handling Field Reports at Closeout

If you act as an on-site representative during construction, or have an on-site rep. on your team, make sure to handle project documentation correctly during closeout. This documentation could include a private field journal as well as notes or documents stored in the representative's computer hard drive. Design professionals are advised to eliminate such items, as well as draft copies of any reports they prepare, because—in the event of litigation—they can be obtained by opposing counsel and be used before the jury. "Why did you make this change?" an architect or engineer will be asked, as the attorney compares a draft report to the final submittal. Witnesses often find it difficult to remember the reasons. Frequently, the person who actually made the changes will no longer be available. This lack of information will then be used to create an image of a design professional who is confused about the issue, or who feasibly may have altered documents in order to avoid liability.

Opposing counsel are completely aware that project representatives often keep their own journals or that daily field reports may still exist in electronic memory. If appropriate, keep the original journal and have the on-site representative erase his hard drive. The unauthorized distribution of documentation can also create problems. Because daily field reports are considered professional instruments of services, they may be changed by the project manager to express a thought in more appropriate language, or to clarify an issue, eliminate an ambiguity, and so on. If one of your project reports seems to contradict something you included in one of the daily field reports, problems could result later. Accordingly, if you give a copy of a field report or similar material to a party on site, these reports could be found in someone else's subpoenaed files and the firm could be asked to explain alleged discrepancies and why you discarded "such important material."

Understanding Completion, Acceptance, and Final Payment

Completion of work under a construction contract is of the utmost legal significance. It ordinarily activates final payment and liquidation of the parties' claims against each other. As a result, your firm must clearly spell out completion in the contract documents.

Completion is usually made up of a two-part process: substantial completion and final completion.

Substantial Completion

Substantial completion occurs when the facility is ready for occupancy, despite defects to be corrected or minor incomplete aspects of the work. Substantial completion is sometimes confused with mechanical completion. Mechanical completion is when the equipment is ready for performance testing.

The resident engineer is required to issue a certificate for substantial completion that establishes the date of substantial completion. The certificate of substantial completion states the responsibilities of the owner and the contractor for security, maintenance, heat, utilities, damage to the facilities, and insurance. In addition, the certificate for substantial completion should fix the time within which the contractor has to complete any unfinished items.

Final Acceptance

Final acceptance considers final payment (including retention) and satisfaction of all contract requirements.

After final inspection and determination that the work has been fully completed, a subcontractor's final release certificate and indemnity is required, with the consent of the surety as the waiver for final payment. The resident architect/engineer then issues a certification of completion and final acceptance. Following this, the resident architect/engineer may be required to file a notice of completion with the county recorder's office.

Either the certificate of completion or the notice of completion can trigger the payment of any remaining amounts due to the contractor. But before such payment is made, the contractor must furnish evidence that material suppliers, subcontractors, and workmen have been paid. The contractor must also furnish a consent to the surety, if any, issuing performance or payment bonds covering the work. If the owner fails to obtain the consent of the surety, he can create a liability to the surety for retainage released if the bonded obligations remain outstanding.

Final payment under this procedure ordinarily amounts to a waiver of further claims by each party against the other. The waiver is subject to stated exceptions on the part of the owner. These include unsettled liens, faulty or defective work appearing after substantial completion, special guarantees running in the owner's favor (such as manufacturer's warranties), and failure of the work to comply with the contract documents.

Six Tools to Control Closeout

One effective way to view project closeout is to think of it as a separate "mini-project" with its own scope, schedule, and budget. The scope of work to close out a design contract is usually well defined in the contract itself. Treating this phase as its own project will help you keep your team members focused on finishing the job.

During this wrap-up period, applying basic project control tools can help you keep your team informed and focused on demobilization and project closeout objectives. These tools can include:

1. **Project completion schedule.** This provides a daily focus on project demobilization and closeout activities. Use this schedule as a communications tool in project status meetings and to assist in establishing plan-of-the-day activities.

2. **Action items list.** Use this to assign responsibility and to track key actions required for closeout. Key points should include: Action Required, Requester, Responsible Individual and Group, Required Date, and Forecast/Actual Completion Date.

3. **Subcontractor punch list.** As with the action items list, use the punch list to track incoming or open

items for a subcontract when the work is essentially complete.

4. **Vendor notification list.** Develop a list of leased or rental agreements, sorted in reverse order by the number of days prior to the projected demobilization date. The list can help you with discontinuation of services or for equipment pick-up. A typical notification list would be organized by the actions required 30, 14, or 7 days prior to demobilization.

5. **Project team de-staffing plan.** As project tasks or phases end, take personnel off the project as soon as practical. The de-staffing plan should reflect remaining job hours and forecast release dates for each individual team member.

6. **Cost control.** During the final project phase, team members must remain focused on cost control and cost awareness. Cost and schedule work together; a shorter schedule usually leads to lower costs, and vice versa. Budget limitations will also focus the team's attention on early completion and closeout actions.

✎ Completing the Construction Phase

After the contractor completes construction, you are responsible for assisting the client in closing out the project. The following tasks are usually included in these efforts:

❑ Receive notification of substantial completion and a list of items to be completed or corrected from the contractor.

❑ Inspect the project with the client for substantial completion. Notify the governmental authorities requiring inspection.

❑ When the project is substantially complete, and it is required by the construction contract, prepare a Certificate of Substantial Completion. Obtain both the client's and contractor's written acceptance and approval.

❑ Ask the client to obtain the Certificate of Occupancy or Occupancy Permit, if required.

   ❑ Obtain from the contractor:

   ❑ Guarantees and warranties

   ❑ Certificates of inspection

   ❑ Operations and maintenance manuals

   ❑ Spare parts

   ❑ Maintenance material stock

   ❑ Record drawings

   ❑ Bonds

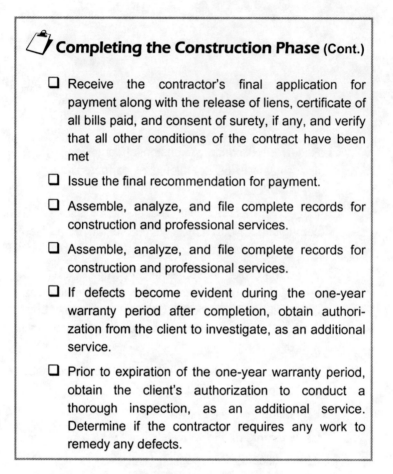

Completing the Construction Phase (Cont.)

☐ Receive the contractor's final application for payment along with the release of liens, certificate of all bills paid, and consent of surety, if any, and verify that all other conditions of the contract have been met

☐ Issue the final recommendation for payment.

☐ Assemble, analyze, and file complete records for construction and professional services.

☐ Assemble, analyze, and file complete records for construction and professional services.

☐ If defects become evident during the one-year warranty period after completion, obtain authorization from the client to investigate, as an additional service.

☐ Prior to expiration of the one-year warranty period, obtain the client's authorization to conduct a thorough inspection, as an additional service. Determine if the contractor requires any work to remedy any defects.

Ten Problems that Prevent Project Completion

To avoid setbacks during the construction phase, all parties need to fully understand the causes of claims. Here are the 10 biggest causes of contract claims:

1. **Delayed Completion.** A late project can have major cost impacts on both the contractor and client. Determination and proof of liability can be difficult. All parties to the contract must take scheduling very seriously and maintain proper job records to support or refute this type of claim.

2. **Changed Time Frame.** Be sure to review any change in the starting or ending date carefully for cost and schedule impacts.

3. **Restricted Work Sequence.** Any sequence of work restriction as a result of existing operation or work of a separate contractor must be clearly stated in the contract documents.

4. **Chain of Command.** Every project has an organizational structure (i.e., supplier reports to sub, sub reports to G.C., etc.) that must not be violated. Prepare an organization chart at the start of the project, and make sure all parties follow it.

5. **Failure to Coordinate.** The client of a multi-prime contract project and the general contractor with several subs have certain duties to coordinate the work. Failure to provide this coordination usually results in cost increases and claims.

6. **Quantity Variations.** Substantial changes in the quantity of work (plus or minus) to be accomplished can greatly affect the unit cost of the work. Address this possibility in the contract with a quantity variation clause.

7. **Quality of Work**. This is very difficult to define in words. Too often the engineer is left to determine proper quality, and this can result in disputes. Where possible, make reference to some existing work or written standard, rather than resorting to the use of terms such as "workmanlike," "reasonable," and "standard for the industry."

8. **Access to Work Area**. Any restriction of access to the work area by one party to another party should be clearly explained in the contract documents.

9. **Failure of Project to Function Properly**. If the contractor is to be responsible for the performance of the project (i.e., watertight walls, rates of production, etc.), then the contractor also must design the work. The contractor cannot be given a detailed set of drawings and specs, be required not to deviate, and then guarantee the results of the engineer's design.

10. **Ambiguous Contract Documents**. Any contract that contains words and phrases that are not clear (i.e., reasonable, timely, workmanlike, etc.) will be subject to interpretation and claims, and final interpretation will usually come from a judge or arbitrator.

Tackling the Project "Red Zone"

One of the biggest problems project managers face at the end of the project is "trailing costs," where the team has reached completion, but hours are still being billed to the project. All too often teams think they're done, but they have a hard time going to the client and cutting it off.

Red Zone Strategies

To keep a tight control on the final phase of the project, you should schedule a "red zone" meeting. The red zone is typically known as the most important part of the football field nearest the end zone that determines the outcome of the game. Similarly, the red zone represents the final phase of your project where you have little space with which to work.

Near the end of the project (ex. 60 days in advance of project completion), the PM should gather team members and ask "What is left to do?" Outline what tasks remain, identify tasks for each person, and set dates for each task. The staff needs to pledge themselves to complete the assigned tasks and not let each other down.

Bringing in New Blood

One of the best ways to tackle the red zone of the project comes from bringing in new passion and energy to the project. D'Alessandro recommends assigning a project closeout task manager.

"Burnout can be a big issue for PMs near the end of the project. There is an opportunity during the red zone to bring in a younger PM who will be excited about working on the project and gaining new experience. Bringing in new blood is a good strategy for finishing the project on time," says D'Alessandro.

If you do bring in a new PM, it is important that you discuss the new team member with the client, and reassure the client that you will still be present on the project. "Tell the client that you have an opportunity to grow a new PM, but you are not going away," says D'Alessandro. "If you have a feeling that the client wants only the "A" team on the project and will be uncomfortable with the scenario, you can still bring in the younger PM, but you will want to make it an internal transition."

However you choose to address the last phase of the project, you need to have a planned vision for completion. Without this extra effort, you may find your projects taking on a life of their own.

Preventing Drag at the Project's End

One of the most difficult activities is to finish the project, get it out the door and close the job number. Many well-managed projects blow the schedule and budget during the final 10 percent of the project. Several of the common pitfalls that must be avoided to prevent "project drag" are:

- A desire to continually improve the project (excess perfection syndrome).

- Fear of failure, which surfaces in an inability to complete the project.

- "Burnout" resulting from too many intensive weeks or months on the project.

- Lack of another project on which to begin work.

- Interest in a new project to the detriment of the existing one.

- Failure to gain closure at the end of each phase and the end of the project.

It may be easiest to view the wrap-up phase of the project as a separate mini-project, with its own scope, schedule and budget. This will help keep the project team focused on the important task—finishing.

A wrap-up project should include the following major tasks:

- Gather all loose ends.

- Evaluate all potential changes and determine which ones should be made.

- Make a checklist of all work to be done.

- Assign final checklist of activities to appropriate team members.

- Back check all items on the checklist until complete.

- Make sure all outstanding receivables are collected.

Demonstrate to all team members, and to the client, that the project is complete by delivering all the final work products as specified by the original contract. In addition, include a final letter to the client in some way specifying that the project has been completed in accordance with the contract. This tells the client the exact project status.

So When is it Really Over?

It is important to understand that there are various stages of project completion. The most obvious is when work has been completed, appropriate documents and reports have been submitted to the client, and, (ideally) everything has been accepted. This completion is considered the "Practical Completion" (all work is done and, under normal circumstances, no additional work is expected to take place).

Of course, invoices or other charges will still trickle in and need to be added to the cost accounting. It is the project manager's responsibility to urge all clients, vendors and sub-consultants to process their demands on the project within 45 days of practical completion.

Frequently the client will have follow up calls, requests for clarification or other loose ends. The project manager should budget for these activities which carry on after the contractual due-date, but he should also determine whether such requests are within the scope of the initial assignment or represent additional work.

"Final Closure" is when the project is closed, and no more charges are accepted. Unless there are unusual circumstances, each project should be closed within 90 days after practical completion.

It's Over When You Complete a Work Stop Order...

Once all final reviews and changes have been completed and the final work product has been delivered to the client, a work stop order should be prepared. This form can be sent to the accounting department and will be used to restrict charging labor or accidental expenses to the job. Charges to the project can then be stopped completely or restricted to certain employees only.

...But Don't Forget Your Records

One final project task that is often overlooked, is records organization. This needs to be done on every job so that files will be orderly, well labeled, up-to-date and easily located—critical when research into the project is needed at a later date.

Frequently, the research is done by someone other than the project manager, so nothing should be left to memory. In addition, a well-organized file can be valuable in reducing the firm's liability in future claims or lawsuits. Don't forget your File Close Out, Plans Close Out, Computer Close Out, and CADD Close Out. Be sure to attend to these before you call it a day.

File Close Out

❑ Gather the work files from all team members along with any office or central files, and combine into one file.

❑ Subdivide the files into logical, clearly labeled subfiles, such as contracts specifications, calculations, correspondence, etc.

❏ Clearly label every item in the file with the name of the person who prepared it, date, job number, description and source.

❏ Throw away duplicate items to save filing space.

❏ Throw away any outdated or revised materials. If it is necessary to keep revised materials, then mark "Revised" or "Superseded" across the front.

❏ Make sure a final copy of all plans, reports, etc., is in the file and in the appropriate drawing storage area.

Plans Close Out

❏ The plan file drawer should be examined and all intermediate drawings discarded. Keep one reproducible copy (Mylar or sepia) of the final plans for record purposes.

❏ Paper prints (progress sets, review and comment sets, estimate sets, etc.) should be discarded.

❏ In some cases, a set of final prints should be sent to the office library for future reference.

❏ Transfer the final plans to permanent storage and log the location in an archive index.

❏ All photos (before, during, after) should be sent to marketing for filing.

❏ One copy of all final reports should be sent to the office library.

❏ General interest or reference materials such as USCGC sheets, flood studies, etc., which have been gathered during the course of the project should be sent to the office library.

Computer Close Out

❑ The project manager or someone designated should review all files on disk, purge all but the latest version of all files and delete all files that are not needed.

❑ Create as an ASCII "read-me" file an index explaining each file's purpose. Include a hard copy with the disks.

❑ Obtain a plastic disk holder and place the disks in a file folder storage box with the other paper file material.

CADD Close Out

❑ CADD drawing that have been manually edited and delivered to clients should ideally be updated with revisions to the electronic file. If these revisions are extensive and updating of the CADD file is impractical, the CADD file should be discarded to avoid future confusion.

❑ In all cases, CADD files should be archived and rendered inoperative by changing the file designation.

For AutoCADD files, change the .DWG file extension to .DWX. When this is done, the file will have to be physically renamed before it can be used by a CADD operator months later, prompting him/her to be advised of its archive status.

Use Project Debriefings to Your Advantage

At the end of every project, you need to conduct a project debriefing with your client. These debriefings provide valuable information for your firm, and they tell your client that you care about their feedback. Project managers at RETEC, an environmental management firm with offices nationwide, practice the following strategies:

- **Start debriefings with the core elements of monthly project reviews.** Since these aspects of the project have been tracked and reported throughout the project, this is a logical place to begin the final debriefing. Then expand the scope of the debriefing as appropriate.

- **Keep the tone of the debriefing positive and forward-looking.** The primary intent is not to find fault, but to learn from any mistakes or shortcomings and apply these lessons to future work. If you put people on the defensive, they won't be very forthcoming with useful information.

- **Focus on the work process, not staff performance.** If there were problems with specific team members, this should be addressed in another forum. Try to depersonalize any criticism to the extent possible.

- **Consider having an outside party facilitate the debriefing.** This can bring a fresh perspective and greater objectivity to the process.

- **Make sure everyone on the team is heard.** Guard against some people dominating the discussion while others remain silent. Encourage everyone's feedback. If someone seems reluctant to share his or her perspective with the group, consider soliciting this input privately.

- **Follow through on actions identified during the debriefing.** Assign responsibility and deadlines for implementing any tasks defined during the meeting, and make sure these are completed. Without action, you minimize the value of project debriefings.

Stick with Your Client after Closeout

Contrary to popular opinion, the job is not over when the project is completed. All too often, the end of the project means the client gets filed away along with the project, yet most disputes crop up after the completion.

Here's the best way to follow up with your client. Practice these, and not only will he be satisfied, he will look to you for his next project.

- Call the client at regular intervals to check in on the project; one New England firm called their clients for three years after a project, at three-month intervals. They reviewed the project, reported on any problems, and assigned blame for those problems. If they themselves were responsible for a problem, they offered to pay for it. The firm had a 90 percent repeat business rate, and had not had a liability claim against them in 26 years.

- Take a look at the lifecycle of the finished project, and let the client know when it should expect to replace a roof vent, re-landscape, fix concrete, etc.

- Know which issues are most important to your client, and report back to him on how these issues are holding up in the project.

- One Midwest firm supplied a maintenance schedule for their buildings to every one of their clients. There were no surprises when it was time for a fix, and the clients knew the firm thought of them beyond the narrow scope of one project.

You may want to reevaluate how much of your marketing goes to repeat clients. Many budgets typically allot 10 percent to repeat clients and 90 percent to new business. This is too disproportionate. If you want your clients to think of you for future projects, stick with them!

Printed in the United States
102417LV00003B/1-69/A